The Talking Stone

An Anthology of Native American Tales and Legends

The Talking Stone

An Anthology of Native American Tales and Legends
edited by Dorothy de Wit

with decorations by Donald Crews

 **Greenwillow Books**
New York

Printed in the United States of America   First Edition
1   2   3   4   5   6   7   8   9   10

Library of Congress Cataloging in Publication Data
Main entry under title: The Talking stone.   Summary: Twenty-seven
tales of Native Americans from nine geographic regions of North Amer-
ica.   1. Indians of North America—Legends. [1. Indians of North
America—Legends]   I. De Wit, Dorothy. II. Crews, Donald.
E98.F6T23   398.2′097   79-13798
ISBN 0-688-80204-4   ISBN 0-688-84204-6 lib. bdg.

Contents

Introduction

THE FIRST AMERICANS WERE A PEOPLE SCATTERED OVER A VAST continent with every extreme of climate from subtropic to arctic; with long seashores, mighty rivers, mountains a mile high, deep craters, and sun-baked deserts. With no means of transportation other than their own feet for hundreds of years, these first people moved across the land, raising families, creating beautiful objects of leather, clay, wood, stone, shell, reeds, and grasses. They had no written alphabets to record their hundreds of different languages, but they carried with them a treasure of myths, legends, folklore, and hero tales. As they moved, they left pictographs on giant rocks, wampum belts and blankets into which they had woven records of customs and events, silver and turquoise ornaments rich in symbolism, and cedar trunks carved into story poles, so that in the last 350 years missionaries, soldiers, folklorists, and writers have as yet only scraped the surface of the folklore of the Native Americans.

On winter evenings, when the season's work was done

and the people were free to relax, the storytellers drew on the folklore of their tribes and told tales. To tell these stories at any other times was thought to be dangerous—the spirits could be angered and send poisonous snakes or drought or some other punishment. Tribal storytellers were also bound by custom as to which stories each might tell; some myths and histories belonged to specific individuals to pass on. Storytellers and shamans were careful to follow all the ceremonial rules, to use precise wordings so that the tales could be given to others in the form approved of by the spirits of the world. Such restrictions might limit the number of tales a given storyteller could pass on, but it also explains in part why some stories were widely known in specific geographic areas and not in others.

The narratives fell generally into three groups: stories of the tribe's creation, histories of tribal heroes, and trickster tales. The peculiar, loveable, foolish, remarkable trickster of the Native Americans acted as go-between for the Above-Spirit, however He might be named, and creatures below. The trickster existed in the days before humankind inhabited the earth, at a time when animals talked with one another. The guise in which he appeared on earth varied from the kindly greatness of a Glooscap to the prankster Coyote. But whatever his name, he became the central figure of whole cycles of stories. Sometimes the tales told how the animals had become what they were; sometimes they explained how the sun, moon, stars, mountains, or rivers came into existence. Sometimes they were meant just for entertainment.

The hero stories were told to instill pride in the deeds of the tribes; they explained tribal ethics and standards of conduct or described religious practices and ceremonials. The language of the Native Americans was dramatic and picturesque; it had rhythm and wit.

Typical of the stories told by most tribes, though in different guises, are those of the Rolling Rock, in which a rock doggedly pursues the individual who has harmed another until he catches him; the Sticky Figure, who is set up to trap the thief who comes to the village water source or the cornfield; the Race, featuring a slow creature (porcupine or turtle) who outwits his speedier rival; the Magic Moccasins, which, when stolen, return to their rightful owner; or the Thunderbird, whose wings create thunder and lightning. Stories of a mortal married to a supernatural being—a star or the sun—were told from the Arctic to the tropics in more than three hundred different forms.

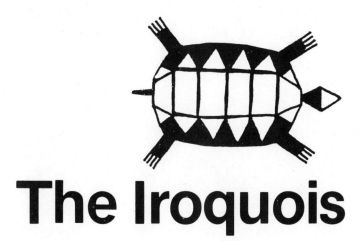

The Iroquois

By the early 1700s the League of Six Nations of the Iroquois formed a sort of island in the midst of the Woodland Tribes of Native Americans. They were different from all the others in the way they lived, in the language they spoke, and in the way they governed themselves. The Onondaga, Oneida, Cayuga, Seneca, Mohawk, and later Tuscarora tribes united to promote the welfare of all their peoples. From the beginning, women were important both in making decisions and choosing chiefs and in establishing the family lines which were traced through the mother's lineage. Marriages were arranged by wives or another mother figure.

Stockades and moats fenced in the villages, and individual longhouses contained many families. In the midst of these there was a community council building surrounded by the cooperative gardens in which melons, squash, beans, and corn supplemented the fish and game the hunters provided. There were great celebrations with dancing, storytelling, and ceremonies to mark the maple sugar, spring planting, strawberry picking, green corn, and harvest seasons.

The Iroquois believed that they were descended from the daughter of a Sky-Chief and the West Wind. They told creation stories of the Great Turtle on whose back the world rested. Many tales centered on the hero figure who had united the different tribes into the league.

Others dealt with the False Face Society, whose members carved weird masks from living trees, to personify the forces of nature. These wooden masks and others woven of tightly twisted cornhusk fiber were used in healing to activate health-giving powers.

There were stories about wizards, witches, and terrifying supernatural monsters or horrible creatures; comic stories that often centered on Turtle, their chief trickster figure.

And among the Seneca in particular, the storytelling would often begin with: "*Hanio!* Let's have a story!" and end with: "*Na-ho!* Story's end!"

The Talking Stone

(SENECA)

IN THE FIRST DAYS, SKY WOMAN DESCENDED TO THE BACK OF
the Great Earth Turtle and began to create the world of men.
Gus-Tah-Ote, the Spirit of the Rock, watched Sky Woman
from the fastness of the huge cliff that loomed like a great
face at the fork of a mighty river. And he sorrowed to think
that for all the ages, he was imprisoned in those cliffs. Then
Sky Woman offered him freedom and told him to choose
where he wanted to live.

Gus-Tah-Ote looked about him and chose the river. But
once in the river, he found that it rolled and eddied and
finally crashed over a precipice as it rushed toward the sea.
Gus-Tah-Ote was terrified and cried out to be saved. And
Sky Woman lifted him out and sent him skyward to become
one with the air. But great winds arose, and storms, and
Gus-Tah-Ote was tossed about and pulled back and forth,
and again he cried out in terror! Then Sky Woman placed
him in a forest, to be one with the earth and the animals.
But the creatures were busy with their young, and the plants

were concerned with multiplying and growing. They did not see the lonely Rock Spirit wandering there. So at last Gus-Tah-Ote went back to the great cliff at the fork of the river to live. There he sat and brooded over what he had seen. The centuries passed, and still Gus-Tah-Ote sat in silence, looking out over the river.

One day Orphan Boy was wandering through the forest. His parents had died when he was a baby, and he had been brought up by the people of his village. The boy had often been ragged and hungry. Now he lived with an old woman who sent him out to hunt for food each day. He already had a string of birds on his back, for he was very skilled with bow and arrows. When he came to the river, he sank to the ground wearily and pulled out a package of parched corn. As he ate, he gazed at the great rock face before him. To his surprise, he heard a voice say, "Would you like to hear stories of the past?" Orphan Boy looked around but saw no one. Again the voice asked, "Shall I tell you tales of long ago?" This time, Orphan Boy looked toward the cliff, for the voice seemed to come from the very rock face itself. A third time the voice asked, "Shall I tell you legends of the days gone by?" Orphan Boy rose. He picked up his string of birds and climbed to the top of the cliff, toward the voice that had talked. He sat in quiet wonder as Gus-Tah-Ote, the Rock Spirit, began: "This happened in the time when men and animals lived as brothers and could understand each other's language. Listen!" The stories flowed one after another until the sun reddened the western sky. Then Gus-Tah-Ote said, "Now leave the birds for me, and return tomorrow."

That night the old woman was surprised at the few birds

Orphan Boy brought home. He had shot only a few on his way back, for his mind had been full of the wonderful tales the Rock Spirit had told him.

The next day the same thing happened. Orphan Boy offered his string of birds and sat and listened as Gus-Tah-Ote spun out his marvelous stories. And again he returned home with few birds.

In the days that followed, Orphan Boy roamed farther and farther into the forest, and soon he did not return to the village even at night. But each day he came back to the rock for the storytelling, which seemed to have no end, and each day he left some small offering of thanks. One day he roamed far to the east. He found himself in a strange part of the forest, at the outskirts of an unknown village, where he decided to stay. At first he was treated as a stranger, but gradually the men of the village began to accept him and to teach him their special hunting skills. He, in turn, took them one day to the great rock, to hear the stories of Gus-Tah-Ote, and after that they went there often.

After a time Orphan Boy decided to get a pouch in which to keep objects that would help him remember the Rock Spirit's stories. He stopped at the lodge where two sisters lived. He asked the younger sister if she would make him one. To his surprise, she brought forth a beautiful bag made of skins. "I have been watching you for a long time," she said. "I have made this pouch just for you. I will make you a deerskin suit as well, and then I would like to marry you and go with you to hear the talking stone." Orphan Boy was very pleased, for he had wanted her as his wife. When the suit was finished, Orphan Boy and the girl left the village and journeyed to the fork in the great river, to the rock of Gus-Tah-Ote. They climbed to the top, made their offering of food, tobacco, and skins, and sat listening to the Rock Spirit. Many days they returned, and each day Orphan Boy placed in the pouch some small objects that would help him recall the wonderful stories he had heard.

One day Gus-Tah-Ote said, "I have finished my stories. Do not forget them. Go back to your people, and tell them, 'This is the way it happened. . . .' Let them come and bring some offering for the storyteller, and let them listen with their ears and their minds, and not sleep. I have spoken."

Orphan Boy and his bride returned to the village of his childhood. He had grown tall and strong, and the people did not recognize him. "I am the one you once called Orphan Boy. I have come back with my wife to bring you a wonderful treasure from Gus-Tah-Ote. Let all the people assemble around the fire, in the meeting ground tonight, and I will relate the stories he has sent you. And because he has said so, let each one bring some small gift for the teller."

That night, when all the people were assembled around the council fire, Orphan Boy took his place before them, and, reaching into his pouch, withdrew an object, and began to speak: "In the far-off days when the Sky Woman descended to the back of the Great Earth Turtle, it is said . . . ." On and on he spoke, one tale after another, just as he had heard them from the talking stone. And the people listened, with their ears and their hearts, and did not sleep.

From that time, from the mouth of Gus-Tah-Ote, say the
people of the longhouse, has come all the knowledge of the
past. From the Spirit of the Rock have come the legends
and folktales the Seneca people still tell to this day.

—RETOLD BY DOROTHY DE WIT

Sky Elk, the Ghost of Whiteface Mountain

(SENECA)

AMONG THE ADIRONDACK MOUNTAINS, WHERE THE FORESTS ARE
still and deep, is one that rises almost a mile high. It stands
somewhat apart, with a lake at its foot. Mists drift across
its slopes and lie wraithlike in its hollows, and men nod
their heads wisely and say, "The Sky Elk is restless tonight.
See, his spirit roams Whiteface Mountain!"

In the days when Turtle ruled the world and men and
animals could speak together, Sky Elk was called O-je-a-neh-
doh by the Seneca. He was stronger and more powerful
than any of the other animals, and he moved through the
forest, tossing his great antlered head in pride. But the day
came when pride made him careless, and as he slept, Gray
Wolf came up and slew him! The Watcher of the Sky World

saw Gray Wolf's treachery, and she carried O-je-a-neh-doh
to the Elk Fields beyond the sun. There he grazed in peace,
and Sky Watcher permitted him to go down to the earth each
night, provided he returned with the dawn. But he was to
take care, for should he three times receive a mortal wound,
he would lose the privilege of returning to earth. And the
hunter who inflicted the fatal wound would instantly pay
with his life.

Thus, over the years, Sky Elk returned each night to his
beloved mountains and feasted on the good green of the
earth.

There came a time when a mighty hunter arose in the
land. He was called Night Wind, and he was more cunning,
more skillful than any other hunter. The first time he
glimpsed Sky Elk, he was astonished at his great size and
soaring antlers. He gazed at him for a long time, and then,
following the hunter's ancient law to warn his prey, he
broke a twig. The huge stag lifted his head and sped away.
Night Wind followed on swift, silent feet. Now and again
he let fly an arrow, but though he saw the stag stumble and
fall, when he came to claim it, the animal had vanished.
Night Wind was puzzled as he returned home.

Days passed into weeks, and the seasons changed from
planting time to harvest. Night Wind was walking in the
cedar swamp one evening as the last rays of the sun pol-
ished the dark leaves. Suddenly he beheld O-je-a-neh-doh
standing silhouetted against the sky in the dusk. The elk's
nose twitched as he caught the hunter's scent, and he
turned to run. Night Wind followed. Hour after hour, as
night deepened and the new moon rose, the hunter pursued
Sky Elk, but when he shot his arrows, they dropped to the

ground, though he saw them hit the stag. At last Night Wind saw him stagger, but for a second time he vanished into the air before Night Wind's very eyes!

The months moved into another season, and the time of the harvest moon was at hand. One day, at full noon, Night Wind saw the stag standing under the shade of a great oak. Sky Elk was blinking, for he had stayed too long on earth, and the brilliant sunlight confused him—in the Elk Fields of the Sky the sun never shone! O-je-a-neh-doh had wandered all night through the dense groves, and now he tossed his antlers wearily. Night Wind crept toward him cautiously but honored the age-old law and rustled a bush. Away sped Sky Elk into the shadows of the forest, through the dim underbrush, up, up the slopes of the mountain lifting its white face to the sky.

A cloud moved across the sky, hiding the sun, followed by another, and another, and yet another until the heavens were black with storm. Winds arose, and the air was heavy with rain. Lightning forked the sky, and Night Wind saw Sky Elk pause, lift his muzzle, and sniff the air. Quickly he let fly his last arrow, and it sped straight to the heart of the great animal. As it left the bow, a terrific crash of thunder shook the ground, and a streak of lightning stabbed the oak under which Sky Elk stood. Night Wind raced to the oak. Terrified, Sky Elk lowered his head and lunged toward the earth, and as he did so, his mighty antlers caught up Night Wind and swept him high into the air. Night Wind shrieked, but Sky Elk, carrying him, rushed toward the mountain and bounded up its white face—higher, higher— until, with one last spring, O-je-a-neh-doh leaped into sky-land.

Dawn stood at the gate of the Sky Fields (though it was not yet her time to appear). Pity filled her heart for Night Wind. She reached out and transformed him into a celestial body—a star brilliant and low-hanging at the very gates of the new day. The Seneca call it Morning Star, and they wait for its appearance to herald each dawn.

Sky Elk fled on, and on, deep into the Elk Fields beyond the sun. But from that time on, he could never again roam the forests and mountains of the earth he had loved, for he had met death for the third time.

Often at night, when the moon rides high over the face of the great mountain, a ghostly form is limned against the shadows, moving like a wraith, from rock to rock. The people know then that the spirit of O-je-a-neh-doh, the Sky Elk, is restless and has come back to guard the earth and bring peace to the animals that still roam the mountains he loved.

—RETOLD BY DOROTHY DE WIT

Turkey Brother and the Magic Panther Suit

(SENECA)

LONG AGO, IN THE FORESTS OF NEW YORK STATE, THERE LIVED an old uncle and his two nephews. They were the last of their village, for war and sickness had wiped out all the others. The elder of the two brothers, Two Feathers, was nearly fifteen, but his brother was still very young. He was called Turkey Brother, for their uncle and Two Feathers had made him a coat from the feathered skin of a large white turkey. When he slipped his arms into the wings, he could fly into the trees nearby and perch there like the turkey whose skin he wore. And he could make gobbling sounds so real that the uncle and Two Feathers were sometimes fooled by him.

Long ago, when a young man reached the threshold of manhood, he would go to the forest or mountain alone, after purifying himself in a sweat lodge. There he would fast and pray until in his dreams an animal came to him, or a bird, or some other living creature. The creature that came would become his protector and helper for the rest of his life. On a day the uncle called Two Feathers to him. "My nephew, it is now time to make your vision quest, to go and find your spirit helper."

So Two Feathers built a sweat lodge, and after he had made himself clean, he went into the deep woods alone, to fast and to pray. At first, nothing appeared to him, but on the tenth day, in his dream, a huge spider dangled itself by a long thread in front of him, saying, "I am your spirit helper. When you are in need, call me, and I will come to you." Then the spider disappeared. Two Feathers wondered indeed how a spider could help him!

But he continued fasting, and shortly afterward in his vision he saw a black snake. It lifted itself up and up until it reached the top of a small tree. "When you wish a protector, call me, and I will come," said the snake, and slid away as silently as it had appeared. Then Two Feathers made his way home, a boy no longer, for the spirit creatures had given him these visions, and he was ready to take up the tasks of a man.

His uncle was glad, and Turkey Brother prepared food for him and made him rest. Then his uncle said, "Now that you have made a vision quest and have found your spirit helpers, you are ready to marry. Alas, there is no woman in our lodge to find you a wife, as is the custom among our people, so you must go forth alone. In a village far to the east there is a great chief who has two daughters. It is my desire that you go there and take one of them for your wife, but the journey there is long and difficult."

Two Feathers resolved to make the trip, for indeed he wanted to marry the daughter of a chief. His small brother ran to him and said, "I will go with you! If Turkey Brother is beside you, you will not have to be afraid!" Two Feathers laughed. He did not wish to take so small a boy with him. But Turkey Brother pleaded so hard and long that at last the uncle and Two Feathers agreed that he might go.

The old man prepared parched corn and pemmican for their journey. Then he said, "Nephew, I have kept little over the years, and now I am old. But in my chest there is a suit fine enough for a man seeking a chief's daughter." He pulled a box from the back of the lodge and drew forth a suit made from the skins of raccoons. But when he held it up to Two Feathers, he shook his head. "No, it is not right," he said, and put it away again. Then he drew out a suit made of finely cured lynx hides. Two Feathers would have worn it gladly, but still the uncle was not satisfied. At last he drew forth a shirt made of black panther skins, with the head of the animal still attached, to serve as a hood. The green eyes glistened, and it would snarl if its wearer were in danger. Fine leggings went with it, and moccasins that would return to their owner if they were stolen. In addition, Two Feathers received a pouch made of fisher skins that would bite if a strange hand reached into it, and a pipe with a carved bear-head bowl, and a snake. The snake would hiss, and the bowl growl, to ward off danger; there was also a medicine root that was ugly but made black wampum if the owner bit its dark end, or white wampum if the owner bit the light end. As for a bow and arrows, the one the uncle chose for Two Feathers was old and shabby so that no one would want to steal it, yet the arrows shot from it never missed their mark.

"My son, you are now ready. There are many dangers waiting for you, and I can warn you, but I will not be able to help you in any way. Should a strange child cry for your help, do not turn from the path to him, for the child is really a wicked wizard in disguise. If you come to a crystal spring, though you are very thirsty, do not stoop to drink, for monsters lurk in its depths and will pull you under. Beware of an old man calling for help. He is a sorcerer and a thief, and he will steal everything you have. Be careful, and let Turkey Brother be your helper on the way." The old man watched as Two Feathers and Turkey Brother set out. So fast did the magic moccasins take Two Feathers that by noon of the next day he had gone as far as most men would have traveled in a year!

Two Feathers did indeed hear a child crying. But Turkey Brother flew on, and Two Feathers followed him and did not stop. At last they came to a spring that bubbled crystal clear out of the rocks. Two Feathers, who was hot and thirsty, stooped to drink. "No!" cried Turkey Brother, but it was too late! A monster sprang at Two Feathers and would have pulled him under, but just in time he was able to grasp it and throw it into a clearing. A second time, and a third time, Two Feathers tried to drink, and each time a hairy hand rose from the spring and lunged at him. But each time Turkey Brother warned him just in time, and he was able to pull the creatures out onto the ground. Finally, the water was safe, and the brothers could drink. Before they continued on their way, they gathered wood and burned the monsters. As the flames mounted, the monsters with a shriek changed themselves into screech owls and disappeared.

Two Feathers and Turkey Brother continued on their way, and at sunset they arrived at a grove of tall trees, in the midst of which stood an old man. "Grandson," he cried, "I am starving, I am dying of hunger! In the tree sits a fat raccoon. Shoot it for me, my grandson! Or I shall perish! Shoot it, I say!"

"No, no, no!" Turkey Brother warned Two Feathers. "Remember what our uncle said. . . ." But again it was too late. Two Feathers had already shot his arrow, and the raccoon toppled over. But the tree had a hollow, and that is where it landed.

"Alas, my nephew! We have lost him," sobbed the old man. "*Aaaaaiiiiii!* I am so hungry—I am starving! Climb into the hollow, my son, and get him out for me! I am too weak!" Two Feathers took off his magnificent panther shirt and leggings so as not to soil them. He placed them, together with his moccasins, pouch, and weapons, at the foot of the tree. Then he climbed into the hollow after the raccoon, but there was no raccoon there! Suddenly he felt himself being pushed down, down, until only a glimmer of light was visible at the top, and under his feet he felt the bones of other victims. Too late he realized that he had been tricked. He heard the old man cackle and the sound of his footsteps running off.

The inside of the hollow trunk was as slippery as glass. There was no way for Two Feathers to climb out. Outside he could hear Turkey Brother wailing. Suddenly he remembered his spider helper. "Ah, spider, come quickly. I need your help," cried Two Feathers.

After a time he felt something brush his cheek. It was a strand of strong spider silk. Soon there was another, and another, until a silken rope reached down from the opening of the hollow. "Climb now," called the spider. And Two Feathers began to climb up, up, but when he was nearly at the top, the rope broke, and he crashed to the bottom.

And now he remembered his second protector. "Ah, black snake! Come and help me," he prayed. He heard a rustling against the tree bark, and the great snake lay at his feet.

"Hold on to me," said the snake, and slowly he pulled Two Feathers up, up through the opening at the top. Turkey Brother rushed to help him out, and the black snake slipped silently away.

But the old man had stolen Two Feathers' clothes and instead had left his own filthy rags and torn moccasins. Two Feathers was forced to put them on, and he and Turkey Brother continued on their way.

The wizard had gone on ahead. As he went along, he discovered that the magic of the panther suit and moccasins was making him younger with each step. He stood erect and handsome when he reached a river, on the other side of which was a village. His voice was strong and commanding when he shouted for someone to come and ferry him across. The chief's older daughter came out of the longhouse and paddled toward him in her own canoe. "I am a great hunter," said the impostor, "and I am looking for a chief's daughter to be my wife."

"I am the older daughter of the chief of this village," said the girl, "and I think you will make a fine husband. I will take you to our lodge." She ferried him across and brought him to the part of the longhouse in which she lived. There was a beautiful couch covered with rich skins. "Here is your place," she said. And the impostor became the husband of the chief's older daughter.

Turkey Brother and Two Feathers made slow progress, for the dirty rags and split moccasins of the thief had made Two Feathers grow gaunt and bent; he wheezed and coughed, and when they at last came to the river, he did not have breath enough to call for the ferry. The impostor caught sight of him and said to the ferryman, "Do not bother to go. It is only a feeble old man and a turkey." But the chief's younger daughter did not like the arrogant way her new brother-in-law spoke, and she crossed over in her canoe.

"We are looking for the chief, for I want to marry one of his daughters," said Two Feathers as they stepped in.

"But you are old! Very old!" said the girl.

"Ah, no, I am not at all old, and this is my little brother. We have come a long journey to your village, and on the way we met monsters at a spring who tried to destroy us. A wizard tricked me, and imprisoned me in a hollow tree, and then stole my clothes and left me his. As you see, the wizard's clothes are magic and have made me as old as he was."

"Ah!" said the girl. "I think the one who wronged you has just become my sister's husband! I will marry you, for I think you speak the truth! The impostor is a danger to the whole village. Come, we must warn my father."

Two Feathers followed the girl to the chief's longhouse. When the other people saw the ugly old fellow, they protested, but the chief said, "My daughter knows what she is about. I shall leave it to her to choose her own husband." So Two Feathers and the younger daughter ate the marriage bread and lived contentedly for some time with Turkey Brother safe and happy on a small shelf in their part of the longhouse. The older sister and her husband, however, scorned Two Feathers and made fun of him. One day, when the impostor reached into the fisher pouch for the pipe, the fisher bit him, and he yelped with pain! He did not see that in his haste the medicine root had fallen out of the pouch. Two Feathers snatched it up and hid it.

Soon afterward he asked his wife to bring him the chief's best bowl; when it was given to him, he breathed into it and bit on the dark end of the medicine root. At once the bowl was filled to the brim with the very finest black wampum. The chief was astonished when he saw it! Not to be outdone, the impostor also demanded the bowl. But when he breathed into it, it overflowed with lizards, toads, and rotten things so foul that his wife had to spend the whole day scouring out the bowl at the river, and the chief looked like a thundercloud.

Two Feathers then took his old bow that the thief had disdained to steal and went out to hunt. He brought back many deer, enough for the entire village, and everyone praised him. On another occasion Two Feathers again asked for the chief's bowl, and after breathing into it, he bit on the white end of the medicine root, and the bowl quickly filled with beautiful white wampum. The chief was so overjoyed he agreed to let the impostor try again when he asked for the bowl. But when the bowl was returned to the chief with maggots, white worms, and decayed food, he was so angry he sent the impostor away from the village for some days.

After a time the chief decided to give a great feast. The whole village was invited. Quantities of deer and other game, pumpkins, beans, squash, corn, and berries were served; the drums beat, and the dancing and singing went on all through the night, and many stories were told about the magic powers of the younger daughter's husband, Two Feathers. When the festivities were over, the people sank exhausted on their couches, happy and well fed.

The impostor was so tired, and he had gobbled down so

much food, that he threw off his clothes and left them on the floor. It was the first time he had taken off the panther suit since he had stolen it.

He slept so deeply that when the morning came and it was time to go to a council meeting, he was still sleeping. Two Feathers was quick to see this. He snatched the panther suit, the pouch, and the moccasins and put them on. Though they had become torn and dirty, as soon as Two Feathers put them on, they became new and clean again, and Two Feathers himself grew young and fresh and as strong as when he had first received them from his uncle. He strode proudly to the council meeting and all the council acclaimed him!

The impostor still snored in the longhouse. His mother-in-law went to waken him and shrieked in terror. "Who is this ugly, strange old man who sleeps in such dirty rags in my daughter's lodging?" she cried. He too had regained his original appearance.

The mother-in-law's cries wakened his wife, and she turned to look at her husband. When she saw him, foul and evil-looking, she dragged him from bed and had him thrown out of the village. "He is no longer my husband! Let him never return!" she said. And he was never seen again.

But Two Feathers received many honors. Not only was he the husband of the younger daughter, but he was a great hunter, a man possessed of strange and wonderful medicine, and he had rid the village of the monsters at the spring and the evil wizard in the woods. In great joy, the entire village returned with Two Feathers and his wife, and Turkey Brother, to the old uncle, and there they lived in peace for many long years.

—Retold by Dorothy de Wit

Central and Northeast Woodland

The Passamaquoddy, Penobscot, Wampanoag, Lenape, Mohegan, Ojibway, Menomini, and many others belonged to the tribes that lived in the area bordered on the east by the Atlantic Ocean and ranged west to the Mississippi, south to Tennessee and North Carolina, and north to the Great Lakes and central Canada. The individual settlements were small; hunting, fishing, trapping, gathering wild rice, and agriculture were the main activities. The influence of the French and the English was pronounced, and the stories often reflect tales told in Europe for centuries, but retold by the Native Americans within the framework of their own cultures, as, for instance, the story of Cinderella.

However, a well-loved cycle of adventures was centered on a hero, a culture figure who was both human and supernatural, both a rascal and a fool, both funny and admirable, both kind and cruel; and depending on which tribe was telling a particular story, that trickster was known as Nanna-

Bijou, Nenebojo, Mana-bus, Winnebojo, Nanabozho, or Manabozho. Most of the tales tell of his giving food to the people, taming monsters, changing the seasons, regulating the winds, originating the rituals or ceremonies and customs, or playing tricks. Or being himself tricked! Blue-Jay (Wiskedjak) and Tortoise are other trickster heroes of these tribes.

The poet Longfellow delighted in the tales he heard about Manabozho, and his famous epic poem *The Song of Hiawatha* is based on them.

"Why" stories are common among the Shawnee, the Winnebago, and the Chippewa; and fantastic giants, strange creatures, and other-world journeys figure in many of their fairy tales and legends. By far the most loved and most familiar, however, are the stories about Manabozho.

Thunderbird

(WINNEBAGO)

WHEN THE EARTH WAS NEW, GIANTS LIVED AMONG THE
people. And the greatest of the giants that then walked the
earth was Nasan. One hundred feet high Nasan stood, and
each step he took was a mile long. Five feet wide was the
space between his eyes, and his mouth, when it was opened,
seemed as large as a valley. His teeth looked like stumps of
bright white birch trees when he smiled. Nasan's dwelling
place was at the end of the earth on a very high mountain
facing the eastern ocean, and his lodge was on the tallest
peak of this mountain where the blue clouds met and
passed each other. Nasan lived there all alone. He was a
lonely giant.

One night around the council fires of the giants, it was
agreed that the Evening Star Lady was the fairest of all
women known to the great ones of the world. The Evening
Star Lady was lovely and bright to see, rising and shining
in the sky each night. The people respected and feared all
great beings—the Great Spirit, all the animal gods, the bird

gods, and the giants also. But they loved the Evening Star Lady.

She was many things to them. Each night the calendar men of the tribes looked to the rising of the Evening Star as the time to make another cut in their calendar sticks. The wanderer, the war scout, and the hunter returning late at night to his home always looked forward to the Evening Star to guide them on the trail. And only to her the young lovers sang happy songs and told the secrets in their hearts.

Now Nasan was lonely. "A pity it is," he said to himself, "that I haven't a wife to mend my moccasins, to keep my lodge in order, and to cook for me." The giant looked up to the sky at the Evening Star Lady, and his heart leaped with delight as he beheld her brightness. At once he knew he had a great love for her. Nasan was determined to have the Evening Star Lady for his wife.

The giant called for the old Needlewoman. Out of the cave where she made her home came the one-eyed Needlewoman. She came with her witching needles, her magic loom, and her buckskin bag of medicine. "Make me wings, grandmother," Nasan said to the Needlewoman. "I wish to go on a journey to the sky." The Needlewoman was very old. Her hair was white, and her one good eye was gray and deep. Old she was, but her hands were quick-moving, and her fingers nimble. In mid-forest by the light of the moon while animal and human slept, the Needlewoman made the wings.

She took one thousand feathers from one hundred wild birds, and she obtained the finest and strongest thread from the gray spiders that lived in the shadowy places of the Gloomy Hills, where the mists linger. The Needlewoman stitched and stitched, and with the thread she bound the feathers together. She deftly wove the silver of the moon-beams, the breath of the fleet deer, and the speed of a dart-ing arrow into the wings. Then the Needlewoman made a paint from the bark of a hemlock tree, and she colored the wings red. She then dipped the wings in the waters of the Great Lake of Salt, and thus, she made the wings strong.

Then the Needlewoman called for Nasan. Only a giant could carry these large, strong wings on his back; but Nasan was the greatest of the giants, and the wings fitted him well.

Nasan soared like a big bird right up to the Evening Star Lady. He brought her a buckskin bag, beaded, and many shells, and he dropped ermine skins and buffalo robes at her feet. Nasan promised the Evening Star Lady he would do anything she wished if she would make her home in his lodge. And the Evening Star Lady smiled at the giant and put her arms around him, and off they flew to his mountain home.

The next evening the Evening Star Lady did not appear in the sky. The night was gloomy, and the people looked and looked. But the Evening Star no longer shone in the sky at night, the night wanderers became lost, the calendar men could not keep the right time, and worst of all, the lovers were dejected. Gone were their dreams, gone were their sweet songs, for gone was their star of love, the Evening Star Lady. There was much sorrow among them.

So they assembled from near and far and cried out to the Great Spirit, who was the ruler of the sky. "Oh, Great Mys-tery, find and bring back for us the Evening Star Lady." The Great Spirit looked over the edge of the sky and heard their cries. The Great Spirit looked into his medicine bag, and saw that the Evening Star Lady had flown off with Nasan, the giant.

Then the Great Spirit ordered Nasan to give her up, and he ordered Nasan to let the Evening Star Lady return to her place in the sky; but Nasan refused. Now the Great Spirit was angry. He rattled his great war drum: *Boom, boom, boom!* The Great Spirit sounded his war cry: *"Hy yi, hi yi, hi yi!"*

Now, Nasan, being a giant, was also a wizard, who knew mighty magic. When he heard the Great Spirit's war cry, he pulled up a tall pine tree out of the ground, and Nasan used the pine tree as he would a pencil to draw a circle around his lodge. Four times he drew a ring around his home and, by placing a strong charm over the inside of the circle, made it a magic zone where no harm could come to him.

The Great Spirit rode the winds to the mountain home of Nasan, and with his hands he shook the mountains. The grass flew, and many trees fell as the mountain rocked. But the grass within the magic circle all around Nasan's lodge stood still, the trees were unshaken, and the giant's lodge did not fall.

The Great Spirit breathed upon the mountain, and his breath was fierce and burning, and out of it there came a roaring fire and smoke that swept over the mountain, scorching all the land before it. But the fire crumbled to cold ashes at the edge of Nasan's circle. Truly there was strong medicine in the giant's magic!

The Great Spirit sent five hundred dark shapes and weird

forms to the home of Nasan, but they could go no farther than the outside of the charmed circle. The Great Spirit sent cold, he sent floods, but these also failed to cross the edge of the ring. It was like a strong wall; nothing could pass it.

Now the Great Spirit, who knew everything, knew that the Evening Star Lady desired above all things a robe of white deerskin. Through the Evening Star Lady, then, he would lure Nasan out from the protection of the magic circle. The Great Spirit went to the chief of the ants and instructed him what to do and say. The chief of the ants took his people to the mountain where Nasan lived, and the ants began to eat holes in the mountain. They bored and bored their way upward until they came right underneath the floor of Nasan's lodge. That night, as Nasan and Evening Star Lady lay down to sleep, they heard voices underneath them. The giant and the Evening Star Lady, like all great beings, knew the language of all creatures, whether human, bird, animal, or insect. So Nasan and the Evening Star Lady put their ears to the earth floor of the lodge, and the words of the ants reached them from the ground underneath their sleeping blankets. "One must see this wondrous white deer for himself," said an ant.

"Is it really all white?" asked another.

"Whiter than snow, silver, or clouds. White beyond all belief is this deer." The ants talked in very loud voices to make sure Nasan and the Evening Star Lady would hear.

"Where does this more-than-snow-white deer live?" one ant asked.

And another answered, "This astounding white deer runs

wild and free in the nearby forest of the hemlock trees."

"Surely," another ant said, "it is the only white deer in the world."

The Evening Star Lady could not sleep that night, knowing there was a white deer nearby, and during the day she could not rest for thinking about the beautiful white robe its skin would make for her. The Evening Star Lady felt she could not live without such a robe. "Husband," she said to Nasan, "I am most anxious for a white deerskin robe."

So great was Nasan's love for the Evening Star Lady and so strong was her wish that he agreed to go on a hunt for the white deer. The giant set out down the mountain for the forest of the hemlock trees. He moved cautiously, knowing the Great Spirit was still on the warpath against him. The Great Spirit, who was hiding behind a gray cloud in the sky, watched Nasan leave his lodge. The Great Spirit was pleased that his plan had succeeded. He knew that no amount of caution could save Nasan from him once the giant left the protection of his charmed circle. The Great Spirit came out of his hiding place in the sky and seized Nasan; with ten thousand phantom hands the Great Spirit held Nasan. Sharper than spears were the Great Spirit's fingers; stronger than the bull moose, stronger even than the oak tree were his hands. With a roar that echoed across the earth, Nasan tried to break away, but the Great Spirit's hands held the giant on all sides. Like ten thousand hammers, the fists of the Great Spirit beat pain against Nasan's bones. Each way the giant turned and fought, he was beaten back by the phantom hands. Nasan clutched at the hands he could not see and grappled fiercely with them, but for every hand he tore away from his body, ten more seized him. The shouts of the Great Spirit and the giant were fearsome to hear, and the earth shook as they struggled with each other. The fight continued from mountain to plain. Four suns, four moons, the Great Spirit and Nasan, the giant, fought each other. Nasan crashed over mountains and staggered backward into the great broad rivers. The Great Spirit marveled at Nasan's strength—truly he was the mightiest of giants!

But the giant fell to the earth at last, exhausted and beaten. The earth shook and crumbled and became a valley where he fell. Thus, the Great Spirit captured Nasan and pulled him up to the sky. The Great Spirit was not cruel or wicked, and he admired those who battled bravely and well. The giant, however, had disobeyed the Great Spirit's command, and brave or not, he must be punished. The Great Spirit changed the giant into a large and awesome eagle. "Your name shall be Thunderbird, ruler of the thunder and lightning. Once the greatest of all giants, you are now the mightiest of all birds," the Great Spirit told Nasan.

The Evening Star Lady was sent back to her place in the sky, and once more there was joy among the people.

Around the world Thunderbird now flies, the maker of the storm clouds and a wanderer of the dark skies. His voice is the noise of the thunder, and the flapping of his wings is the flash of the lightning.

—ADAPTED FROM THE THUNDERBIRD AND OTHER STORIES
BY HENRY CHAFETZ

Little Burnt Face

(ALGONQUIN)

IN THE DAYS OF OUR GRANDFATHERS THERE WAS A LARGE LAKE surrounded by birch forests. On one side of the lake there was a village in which lived a man and his three daughters. The older girls were capable and good-looking, but they were concerned only with themselves. The youngest was very pretty, but she was shy and frail. Her mother had died when she was born, and in his sorrow, the father often went on long hunting trips, leaving the girl in the care of the older sisters. And since they wanted to be free to do as they chose, as the years passed they left more and more of the household chores for the youngest. Sometimes the small girl stumbled under the heavy loads of sticks for the fire; sometimes she was bent almost double under the weight of heavy water carriers. And she was often so tired grinding corn and preparing the food for her sisters that she sat alone by the fire, not even wanting to eat. Then the sisters would laugh at her, mock her ragged dress, and more than once would push her so close to the fire that the hot ashes flew up and burned her face and arms, and the hot coals scorched her feet. Sometimes the hot sparks flew into her hair and singed it so that it was scraggly and rough. The villagers looked at her singed hair and burned skin and they laughed and called her Little Burnt Face. When the father returned from his hunting and questioned the older girls, they would tell him that the little girl was careless and did not obey their warnings and often went too near the fire or hurt herself in other ways.

Little Burnt Face did not complain, but she was lonely and wished her father were at home more often. One time, when he returned from a hunting trip, he brought back a quantity of the white shells from which wampum was made. The girls set about stringing the pretty shells. Little Burnt Face also made strings of them, hoping that when she wore them, they would hide some of her scars.

At the far end of the lake there was a large lodge in which there lived a strange and mysterious person. His sister kept his wigwam for him, and when the red sun laid a path from the west across the lake to his doorway, the villagers could hear the lapping of the water against his returning canoe. They could see the game—deer, squirrel, rabbit, or fowl— that he dropped in front of the wigwam. They could see the moccasins his sister hung for him. But he himself was not to be seen. It was rumored that he was wonderful and strong, and they called him the Invisible One. Great was the curiosity of every maid in the village, for it was known that he sought a wife. However, he would accept only the one who could see him as he truly was. His sister let it be known that any girl in the village might come to the lakeside at sunset when her brother returned each day. But it would be the maid who could say what he used for his shoulder strap, and what his bowstring was made of, who would become his wife.

Every evening some of the girls would braid their hair with shells and beads, don their best robes, and go to the lakeshore. But as yet not one of them had known the answer or seen the Invisible One.

One day the two older sisters made themselves lovely and dressed their hair till it shone. At sunset they went to the great one's sister and waited for the splashing sound of his paddle. When they heard it, the Invisible One's sister asked, "Do you see my brother now? Do you truly see him?"

Both girls answered at once, "Yes. Indeed we see him," though they saw nothing at all.

"And of what is his bowstring made?" she asked.

One of the girls said, "It is a green withe of the ash tree."

And the other girl said, "It is made of rawhide."

Both materials were commonly used to make bowstrings. But the sister of the Invisible One shook her head and led them back to their own wigwam. "You did not truly see my brother," she said.

The sisters were cross and unhappy. They vented their temper on Little Burnt Face, pushing her into the hot coals till she cried with pain.

Nevertheless, on the following day Little Burnt Face rose early before the others wakened and bathed in the lake. She too wished to visit the lodge of the Invisible One. But though she was clean, her rags were so ugly! She went deep into the birch forest and pulled off large sheets of the white outer bark of the trees, saying as she did so, "My brother birch tree, give me some of your fair white skin that I may make a dress for myself and not be shamed! I will stitch flowers and birch leaves around its hem to make it beautiful!" And Little Burnt Face scraped on the thin birch bark figures of the forest creatures and flowering vines. Then she sewed the strips of bark together to make a loose gown, which she tied with a sash made of leaves and strong vine fibers woven together. She put flowers in her singed hair and a string of the wampum shells around her neck, but for her bare feet she had only a pair of her father's large old moccasins that had to be tied on lest they fall off her feet. She made her way to the lakeshore amid the laughter and scorn of the villagers. Her sisters mocked her: "Oh, indeed the Invisible One should see this! He'll paddle to the other side of the lake very quickly!" But Little Burt Face lifted her singed head and scarred face proudly and walked on in the direction of the great wigwam as the sun was setting.

The sister of the Invisible One saw her coming; she heard, too, the laughter of the others, and she went out to greet Little Burnt Face. "You too wish to meet my brother? Come, let us wait here at the water's edge. We shall soon hear the sound of his paddle."

Little Burnt Face waited with her, half afraid and shy, but eager to see if she might catch a glimpse of the great one. In time, there came the sound of water lapping against a canoe and the drip of water falling from a paddle. "Now, Little Burnt Face! Look into the sun! Do you see my brother?"

Burnt Face leaned forward, and her eyes searched the water; then a strange glow spread across her face! It was a glow of amazement, of wonder. "Yes—ah, yes! I do see him! How great he is—how beautiful!"

The sister asked, "If you see him, tell me of what his bowstring is made?"

For a moment Little Burnt Face was still; then she said, "It is—yes, I am sure it is—the rainbow!"

Surprise flickered over the sister's face, and she asked

again, "And his shoulder strap with which he pulls his game —of what is that made?"

Little Burnt Face shook her head. "It cannot be, yet I think truly it must be—the Milky Way itself! Ahhhh—what a great, great wonder!"

Then the sister smiled with joy and turned Little Burnt Face toward the lodge. "My child, it is indeed as you say. My brother, the Invisible One, will come shortly to our lodge, and we must be ready for him. Come, let us prepare ourselves." So saying, she brought Little Burnt Face to the lodge. She prepared warm water scented with herbs and pine resin, and as she bathed the girl, all the ugly scars disappeared. Then she washed the scraggly stiff hair and combed it softly with a comb from her own chest, and as she combed the hair, it grew longer and longer and shone like the wing of a blackbird! From her chest, she brought out a gown of softest white deerskin, finely beaded, and on Little Burnt Face's feet she placed small moccasins embroidered and quilled. Little Burnt Face shone with a beauty no one had seen before!

The sound of footsteps approaching brought the sister to the opening of the wigwam. She pulled Little Burnt Face forward to meet the Invisible One, for suddenly the girl felt shy and lowered her eyes.

"So we have found each other at last!" The voice was deep and quiet.

Then Little Burnt Face felt such a rush of joy she put out her hands and laughed! "Yes!" she said. "Yes, we have found each other!" She moved to his side and sat beside him in the wife's place as the darkness fell across the water.

—Retold by Dorothy de Wit

Ojeeg, the Hunter, and the Ice Man

(MICMAC)

ON THE SHORES OF A LARGE BODY OF WATER, NEAR THE GREAT evergreen forests of the north, there lived a hunter with his wife and young son. Their wigwam stood by itself, far from the village, and they were very content, for Ojeeg was skilled with his arrows and brought as much game and furs to his wife as they had need of! The little boy would have been happy, indeed, if the snow had not been so deep or the winters so long. He did not miss companions to play with, for his father showed him the tracks of the grouse and the squirrels. He pointed out the white coats of the rabbits and the weasel, and he trained him to use his bow carefully so that he would not waste his arrows.

But the cold grew more bitter as the long winter months dragged on. One day the boy saw a squirrel running around a stump, looking vainly for buried nuts, for the snow was too deep. Finally, the squirrel rested on his bushy tail, and as the boy came toward him, he said, "I am hungry, and there is no food to be found anywhere! Aren't you, too, tired of this ice and cold?"

"I am," said the hunter's son. "But what can we do against

the power of the Ice Man? We are weak; he is cruel and strong!"

"You can cry! You can howl with hunger!" replied the squirrel. "Your father is a great hunter. He has strong power, and maybe he can vanquish the Ice Man if he sees your grief. Cry, cry, small brother! It may help!"

That night the young boy came into the wigwam, threw down his bow and arrows, and huddled beside the fire, sobbing. He would not answer his mother when she questioned him, and he would not stop crying. When his father came home, the boy's cries grew even louder, and nothing would make him stop, until at last the hunter asked, "Is it perhaps that you are lonely? That you do not like the snow and the cold?" At that the boy nodded his head. "Then," said the father, "I shall see if I have the power to change it."

He went out the next day on his snowshoes. Long he traveled by the frozen water till he came to a narrow place that was choked with huge blocks of ice. He took his sharp knife and a stone chisel, and he began to dig away at the chunks. Many hours he chipped and hacked and pummeled the ice, and in the end he heard the barricade crack! The ice began to move, and a part of it broke off and jostled and bumped around until more cracks appeared. The whole mass of ice began to float slowly away. The hunter rested and wiped the sweat from his face. Then he heard the voice of Peboan, the ice king, piercing the air: "You have won for now, my son! You are strong indeed, and your Manito power is great! But I shall gain the final victory, for next year I will return, and I will bring even more snow! The North Wind will blow more fiercely, and the trees will break with the weight of the ice I will pile on their branches! The waters will freeze so that no matter how many warriors cross them, not a crack will appear. Then you will see, grandson, who is the master of winter!"

The hunter returned to his wigwam. The snows were now melting, and green was returning to the earth. Sweet sap rose in the maple trees, and his little son shouted with joy! But the hunter remembered the threat which the ice king had made: "Next winter will be worse—much worse!"

So he set himself to cutting wood and piling it in great stacks; he gathered the resin from the pine trees and formed it into great lumps. From the game which he brought home he extracted much fat, and this he rendered and stored in large oil pots. Baskets of evergreen cones and thick logs he stored up also. Then, when the maple and the oak flaunted their red and yellow banners at the dark hemlocks, he went somewhat apart from his own lodging and built a small, very tight new wigwam. He left his wife warm skins and food in quantity; then, with supplies for himself, he began stacking them, and the firewood, the resin lumps, the oil pots, and the baskets of cones, within his new lodging.

When the first snowfall whitened the ground, he bade his wife and son have courage and went to the new wigwam. He laced the skins tightly and closed the opening securely. With food and water at hand and warm furs to cover him, he built a very small fire in the center of the fire hole and sat down to wait for Peboan.

At first the frost was light, and the snow melted quickly. At night the wind did not rise much, and the hunter thought, "Perhaps I have frightened old Peboan away! He will see that it is not so easy to win over me!" But as the winter deepened, the tent poles rattled more, the skins shuddered a bit, and it took more fire to warm the wigwam. Still, Peboan did not come. The hunter heard the great owl swoop through the trees at night. He heard weasels and rabbits move through the snow, and once the heavy footfall of a moose crashed through the drifts. The cold became intense.

Then, suddenly one night, the skins across the door opening were torn away, and a gust of North Wind almost blew the fire apart! Peboan stood there, grizzled and bent. His face was lined and cruel, and his long beard hung with icicles. "I have come as I said I would," he shouted.

The hunter rose swiftly, tied up the door skins, and put more wood on the fire. A chill ran through him—the ice king's power was very great! "Grandfather, be seated at my fire. You are my guest here!" he said. The old one sat far from the fire and watched him.

"My power is great! I blow my breath—the streams stand still; the waters are stiff and hard like rock crystal!"

The hunter shivered and put another log on the fire. "The snow covers the land when I shake my head; trees are without any leaves, and their branches break with the weight of my ice!"

The hunter added some cones, and the flames leaped up. "No birds fly now, for they have gone far away. Only the hardy ones flit around, and they are hungry."

The hunter added more wood to the fire, for the air in the wigwam was becoming bitter cold, and frost hung on his eyebrows and nose. "The animals hide away and sleep through the long cold." Peboan laughed grimly as he saw the man draw his fur closer around him.

"Even the hunters do not leave their lodges. The children curl deep into their blankets for warmth and cry with hunger."

Then Ojeeg pulled out the resin lumps; first one, then another he tossed into the coals, and they burned hotly. Peboan shook his white head and moved as far away from the heat as he could. When the hunter saw that, he added yet another clutch of pitch and more logs. Sweat began to roll down the wrinkled face; the ice king huddled close to the wall of the wigwam; his icy garments began to melt.

Ojeeg took up the pots of oil and poured them onto the fire. The flames burned orange and red and blue! They licked at the old man's long robe, at his ice-covered feet, at his snowy mantle, and the Ice Man cried out in pain, "Enough, enough! I have seen your power, Ojeeg! Take back your fire and heat! Stifle your flames!" But the hunter only built up the fire higher, and the Ice Man became smaller and smaller, till at last he melted into a pool of water which ran over the ground and out, under the wigwam opening. When he saw that, Ojeeg, the hunter, untied the skins and looked out. The Ice Man was gone completely! Beyond his doorway the ground was brown and soft with pine needles, he could hear running water, and birds flew through the treetops. How long had he been in his wigwam? The spring was at hand!

Ojeeg put out his fire and ran toward his wife and son, who had come out and stood waiting to welcome him! The ice king would not make so long a visit next year! Only the white flowers of the snowdrop, fragile and small, remained to mark where Peboan had left his footprints!

—Retold by Dorothy de Wit

Southeast

Stretching from the forested Smoky Mountains to northern Alabama, west to the Mississippi, and south into the swamplands of South Florida and the Gulflands, the Southeast incorporated many cultures: Cherokee (*Tsalagi*, Cave People), Creek, Choctaw, Biloxi, Caddo, and others. The area encompassed hundreds of orderly villages, each with community fields and gardens, a council house, and a lacrosse field. Long association with English and Spanish explorers and settlers, with the black slaves of the southern colonies, and with the Central American Indians as well strongly influenced their customs and stories.

Southeastern tribes are not as famous for their rock carvings, story poles, wampum belts, and blanket designs as were some other tribes. Their stories were passed on orally, but by the time De Soto invaded the Southeast in the sixteenth century, work had already begun on a phonics alphabet. By 1823 Sequoyah, a Cherokee, had perfected a Cherokee language syllabary and was able to record in writing legends and tales. And by the latter part of the 1800s Anglo-American scholars were living among the Cherokee, studying and recording their folklore. They were especially interested in the trickster tales of Rabbit, Frog (the council leader), and the other creatures of the Snowbird Mountains area. These tales, widely published, often had as their themes the Creation, medicine beliefs, the discovery of fire, of the stars and moon, and an explanation of how animals and birds got their shapes and colors. There were also "wonder tales," usually about witches, ghosts, or spirit figures.

When the U.S. government forcibly removed these southeastern tribes to the Oklahoma Territory (1832–39), thousands died. History records the event as the Trail of Tears. But even this did not eradicate their remarkable stories, which are still to be found among their descendants, almost unchanged, in Oklahoma and in the adjoining tribal areas.

The Theft of Fire

(HITCHITI)

IT WAS RABBIT WHO RAN AWAY WITH FIRE AND SCATTERED IT.
At that time people were forbidden to build a fire except
in the busk ground. It was the custom to build a very big
fire there when a dance was to be held.

Rabbit knew when there was to be a dance, and he
thought, "Hah! I will go there and dance, and I will run
away with some of that fire!" Then he planned how he
would do it. First he gathered a handful of the sticky resin
from the pine trees; then he rubbed his hair with it. All over
his head he smeared the tarry gum till every hair stood up
like a porcupine quill.

When he had decorated himself for the dance, he started
out for the busk ground. Many people were already there
when he arrived. Rabbit took a seat apart from the crowd,
but when his friends saw him sitting by himself, they went
to him and said, "Now, Rabbit! You are a good dancer, you
know how to lead, so you must lead our dance!"

Rabbit agreed, and as he led the dancing, he began to

sing. The dancers followed, and when he saw that there was a large group behind, he began to stomp and to leap, singing loudly all the time and moving in a circle around the great fire. Faster and faster he led the dancers, closer and closer to the fire. He threw back his head and then bowed it low in front of him, moving ever closer to the flames. Some of the dancers imitated him, but none dared come as close to the fire as he. Others laughed and said, "That is Rabbit who dares go so near the flames! He always does that, does Rabbit!" Rabbit kept circling faster and faster and bowing lower and lower. Suddenly, before anyone knew it, he had poked his resined head right into the fire! Away he ran, with his head in flames. Everybody began to shout, "Hulloa! Catch him! Throw him down! He has stolen our fire!"

They ran after him, but Rabbit ran faster and faster, until he disappeared! The people looked for him in all the places they could think of, but Rabbit was not to be found.

Then the people said, "The fire is in the resin on Rabbit's head. Let us call forth rain to put it out." So they chanted and called on the rain spirits to help them, and the skies opened. Rain came down in great drops. All day it rained, and all night, and again the next day and night, till the forest was glistening and very wet. On the fourth day the people said, "Surely by now the rain has put out Rabbit's fire!" and they asked the rain to stop. The sun shone, and the weather was fine. But sly Rabbit had found a hollow tree and had stayed in it safe and dry. Now Rabbit came out, and he built a little fire here, a little fire there. And he laughed at the people who tried but could not catch him. Again they called down the rain, and the skies grew dark.

But Rabbit ran and hid in his hollow tree and kept his own fire burning.

Once again the people let it rain until they were sure Rabbit's fire was out. But when the sun appeared, there was clever Rabbit, again setting fires. And so it went for some time, with the skies pouring forth rain and puddles lying all around, yet when the downpour was over and the sun made shadows on the open spaces, Rabbit lit small fires in the dry places. Nothing could stop him.

At last the people saw that Rabbit was too cunning for them! So they gave up, and each went back to his own lodging place, even the Keeper of the Dance Fire. Rabbit had spread fire far and wide and hidden sparks in many pieces of wood.

This is the story told by our old men about how Rabbit stole fire and passed it on to all the people. And to this day, if you will rub dry sticks together for a long time, the sparks of fire that Rabbit stole and hid there will burst out and make a flame for you!

—Retold by Dorothy de Wit

Killarney Secondary School

Spearfinger, the Witch

(CHEROKEE)

THIS IS WHAT THE OLD MEN TOLD ME WHEN I WAS A BOY. . . .

Hi-la-hi-yu, a long, long time ago, a terrible witch roamed over the Blue Ridge Mountains and the Smokies. Her only food was human livers. She liked them best young and tender. She was a magician and a clever one. When she came into a settlement, she could swiftly change herself into a human shape. In such a disguise no one could recognize her as the witch she really was.

Most of the time she looked like just an ordinary old woman, except that the skin of her body was hard as rock— so hard that an arrow could not pierce it—and the forefinger of her right hand was made of stony bone, and it always pointed outward from her fist like the head of a spear. Whenever she got near enough to anyone who had strayed out alone from the village, she stabbed that person with her frightful finger. That is why the people called her U-tlun-ta, Spearfinger.

Spearfinger was always hungry, so she wandered over the mountains in all seasons and in all kinds of weather, looking for food. Her favorite haunts were the dark gaps of Nantahala or the Chilhowee Mountain where it falls to the river on the Tennessee side of the Smokies.

Now, there was a day when to help her get over rough country more quickly, Spearfinger decided to build a great stone bridge high above the ground from Tree Rock on the Hiwassee across to Whiteside Mountain in the Blue Ridge. She had such magic powers over any kind of stone that she could carry in her arms great boulders as if they were only pumpkins. And she could stick them together merely by striking one rock against the other. She had partly finished the bridge when a bolt of lightning struck it and scattered the pieces all along the ridge down from Tree Rock. Anyone who climbs the mountain can still see the rocks today just as they fell long ago.

The people were afraid of Spearfinger and her evil appetite. They never knew when she might come among them and in what disguise.

One day an old woman appeared near the village on a trail where children were gathering strawberries and playing games with pebbles. She sat down on the grass close by, and her eyes shone like fire coals in her head as she watched. Presently she spoke in a soft, coaxing voice: "Come to me, my grandchildren, come to your granny, and let granny comb your pretty black hair." And one of them hurried to her and laid her head in the old woman's lap. The granny sang a song, *su-sa-sai, su-sa-sai,* as she combed the child's hair with the fingers of her left hand until the child fell asleep. Then, with her sharp stone finger which she had kept hidden in the folds of her dress, Spearfinger pierced the little one through, took out her liver, and hurried off to eat it.

Sometimes Spearfinger conjured herself to look like some

member of a family who had gone from the house on an errand. The old witch entered the house and waited for a chance to stab someone with her long, cruel finger and take the liver for food. The person would not even notice because Spearfinger knew how to work her magic in such a way that there was no pain nor any wound. But as the days passed, the person would sicken, grow weaker and weaker, and die. The medicine man could do nothing, and no one knew that it was because Spearfinger had taken the victim's liver.

When the frosts came in the fall, the villagers went into the woods to burn the leaves so that they could find all the chestnuts that had fallen to the ground. Spearfinger knew this, and at sunrise each morning she stood on a high rock cliff, turning her head this way and that until she saw smoke rising from the leaf fires. Then she climbed down the mountain in the direction of the smoke. The villagers were busy filling their baskets. Spearfinger would try to surprise one of the chestnut pickers who had wandered off from the rest. But the people knew this, so they kept together while they worked, and they watched closely to see that no stranger approached them. If one of them went down to the spring for water, when he or she returned, the rest were always afraid that it might be the liver eater in disguise.

Most times, as she prowled the mountains, Spearfinger kept her true form. It happened that a lone hunter would catch sight of an old woman with a queer, pointed hand swinging heavily at her side. As she passed through the deep woods, she pushed great rocks out of her path, and all the while she sang to herself in a low voice, *"Uwe-la na-*

tsi-ku, liver, I eat it. *Su-sa-sai, su-sa-sai."* The tune was rather pretty, but the hunter would feel his blood run cold. He knew it was the liver eater, and he would crouch behind a big tree until the witch had disappeared.

At last the chiefs called the people together in a great council. Old men and young men talked. It was decided that the best way to kill Spearfinger was to trap her in a pitfall so that all the warriors could attack at once. They chose a trail between two villages, and there they dug a deep pit. They laid brush across the top and then covered it with grass and leaves so that the witch would not know the ground had been disturbed.

The warriors with bows and arrows hid themselves in the woods beside the trail. They had not long to wait before an old woman came walking slowly toward them along the path. She looked like one of the old women they knew in the village, but they guessed that she was Spearfinger because she held her hand hidden under her blanket. She stepped onto the brush and fell with a crash into the deep hole below. Instantly the frail old woman turned into the terrible liver eater that she really was with skin like gray stone and her pointing finger jabbing in every direction.

The warriors rushed out and surrounded the pit. They aimed and shot well, but their arrows broke against Spearfinger's stone skin and did not harm her at all. Spearfinger taunted them in a screeching voice and clawed at the side of the pit, trying to climb out. As the warriors talked about what to do, they heard a bird singing in the branches of the tree. It was Ut-su-gi, the titmouse, and it sang *un-un-un, u-na-hu,* which means heart. Several of the warriors took the bird's advice and aimed their arrows at Spearfinger's heart. Seven arrows were shot, but each one glanced off with its flint head broken.

The warriors were angry at the bird. One of them caught the titmouse and clipped off the tip of its tongue. And ever since the titmouse has had a short tongue and people say it tells falsehoods.

Some of the men suggested that they throw flaming logs on the old witch. But others said it would do no good because the witch was made of stone and would not burn. As they argued, Tsi-ki-li-li, the chickadee, flew from a branch straight toward Spearfinger and alighted on her right hand. The warriors took this as a sign that their arrows should be aimed there. Tsi-ki-li-li was right. Spearfinger kept her heart on the inside of her stone-fingered hand, which she held knotted into a fist.

Now the old witch became wild with fright and jumped about in the pit in an effort to escape the arrows— and she thrust her sharp finger wickedly at anyone who came near. But the seventh arrow of the strongest warrior struck the witch's stone finger where it joined the palm, and she fell down dead.

There was great rejoicing, and from that day on the chickadee was respected as a truth teller. When a man was away from his village on a dangerous journey, his friends were not afraid for him if the chickadee came to perch near his house and sang *tsi-ki-li-li, tsi-ki-li-li.* . . .

That is what the old men told me when I was a boy. . . .

—FROM JOHN RATTLING-GOURD BY CORYDON BELL

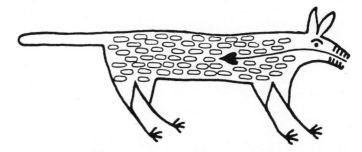

Southwest

The mesas, deserts, canyons, mountains, and river valleys of Arizona and New Mexico are the homes of some of the oldest Native Americans in our country. The Pueblo people came from what is now Colorado between A.D. 1050 and 1300. They built their packed earth (adobe) multiple dwellings entered by house ladders on the dry mesas. In the center of each pueblo was the underground kiva, where the men and elders met for discussion and for ceremonials.

The Pueblo people used colorful kachina masks and ceremonial dress to summon the help of the kachina spirits, messengers who carried their prayers to the attention of higher spirits. Many of their stories tell about these ceremonial practices.

Another cycle of stories had Don Coyote (Señor Coyote or plain Coyote) as trickster hero, and a third series featured Grandmother Spider, the tiny creator-magic maker. The Pueblo and Hopi tribes traced their beginnings through a series of worlds, one above the other. These Creation myths were long and involved, but the main themes of Mother Earth-Father Sun or Sky, huge prehistoric monsters, and trips to other worlds were common to many of the southwestern tribes, though details varied. Such myths and legends became part of the ceremonies that called down rain, celebrated the young corn, announced the coming of age of girls and boys among the Hopi, Yuma, Zuñi, Pima, and Pueblo tribes.

In the Southwest were also the Navajo, the Comanche, and the Apache Native Americans. Sheepherders, cattlemen, and horsemen now, they had resisted fiercely the white invasion. The Navajo named themselves *Dineh*, the people; many of them lived in hogans scattered over their vast desert domain, caring for their flocks, weaving stories and symbols into colorful blankets, creating beautiful silver and turquoise jewelry. The Navajo are leaders among the Native American peoples, and they maintain many of their traditions; their medicine men and storytellers still recite the Creation myths, make sand paintings, rich in color and symbols, and continue to tell Coyote stories.

In the hidden valleys of the canyon areas and along the Gila and Colorado rivers the Havasupai, Hualapai, Yavapai, and Maricopa farm small plots and produce beautiful basketry, but because of their remoteness, few of their tales have been translated into English.

Foot Racers of Payupki

(HOPI)

In the old days, as is known, there were two villages, one named Payupki and the other Tikuvi. Payupki was the smaller, and Tikuvi the larger. In Tikuvi there were many good foot racers, but in Payupki there were few.

One day the chief of Payupki saw the people of Tikuvi going out to their running grounds to have races. He sent for a certain boy in his village. He said to him, "The people of Tikuvi are racing today. I would like to know how good their runners are. You are the best runner we have in Payupki. Go down and join them. Run with them; let me know what you learn."

The boy runner of Payupki went to the Tikuvi races, and the people welcomed him and invited him to join the contest. So he ran in the long race. The best runners of Tikuvi were in it. At first the boy from Payupki was far behind. But as the race went on, he moved forward. There were two runners ahead of him. Then there was only one. He desired to win, but he remembered that the chief had told him only to get information about the Tikuvi runners. So he allowed the Tikuvi runner to finish first. When the racing was over, the Payupki boy returned home.

He said to the chief, "I went to the running grounds. I joined in the long race. Though I finished second, I believe I could have won. But I did not press on."

The chief answered, "You have told me what I wanted to know. Someday we shall run against Tikuvi. Meanwhile, train yourself and make your legs strong."

So the boy trained himself. Every day he went running. He ran across the mesa; he ran on the low ground; he ran in the hills. He felt himself grow stronger. And one day the chief of Tikuvi came to Payupki. He found the chief of Payupki down in the kiva. He entered. They greeted each other, and they smoked together. When the tobacco was consumed, the chief of Payupki put the pipe away. He said, "We are glad you have come. What is in your mind?"

The chief of Tikuvi answered, "I came to tell you that four days from now my village will have a racing festival. We would like to have you come with your best runners. Bring whatever you wish for betting; we shall do the same."

The chief of Payupki said, "We are a small village. We have only one good runner here, the one you know about. We shall bring him."

It was arranged. The night before the races were to take place, the men of Tikuvi went into their kiva to discuss the contest. One of them said, "The boy from Payupki may beat our runners. We may lose whatever we have bet."

Another said, "You forget that he ran against us before

and did not win. Why should we be concerned?"

They argued this way back and forth and decided at last that there was nothing to fear from Payupki's single runner. While they sat there talking, Spider Grandmother came with her medicine bag. She descended to the first level of the kiva, and as she started down toward the lower levels, the men shouted at her, "Go away, Grandmother."

She stopped, saying, "I have come to give help to our runners. I have brought medicine to put on them."

They replied, "Go away, Grandmother. Our runners don't need your help."

She said, "When you are in trouble, you send for me, but now you say, 'We don't need you, Grandmother, go away.' It is you who have said it. Therefore, I shall leave."

She climbed the ladder and went out of the kiva. She went to her house on the edge of Tikuvi and gathered her things together. Then she left Tikuvi and went across to the village of Payupki. When she arrived in Payupki, the people welcomed her and took her to the kiva, where the men of the village were discussing the next day's contest. Spider Grandmother began to go down the ladder. Seeing her coming, the men called out, "Come down, Grandmother." She sat with them. The chief gave her a pipe to smoke, and she smoked energetically. She blew great clouds of smoke from her mouth. The men smiled, thinking, "Spider Grandmother is old. She takes in too much smoke. In a few moments she will become dizzy and fall over." But Spider Grandmother did not fall over. She blew out more clouds of smoke and after the tobacco was finished, she returned the pipe to the chief.

He said to her, "You are welcome here. Why have you come?"

She replied, "I lived in Tikuvi. I went to the kiva to give help to their runners who will race tomorrow, but the men laughed at me. They said, 'Go away, old woman.' So I left Tikuvi. I have come to your village, and now I will help your runner."

She took a bowl from her bag. She put a magic powder in it, she added water, and she made medicine. She said, "This is to protect your runner against sorcery." They brought Payupki's boy runner into the kiva. Spider Grandmother rubbed the medicine on his legs. Then she said, "In Tikuvi they will sit up all night celebrating. Here in Payupki we should sleep."

The chief said, "Spider Grandmother speaks truth. Let us sleep."

The people found a room in the village for Spider Grandmother. They built a fire in it to warm her. They brought blankets for her. Then the village of Payupki slept.

The next morning the men and boys gathered and went to the Tikuvi racing grounds. "Where are the runners?" the chief of Tikuvi asked.

The best runners of Tikuvi came forward. The boy runner of Payupki came forward. The men of the two villages began to make bets. They bet whatever they had brought—moccasins, belts, shawls, kilts, even bows and arrows. The first race began. The boy from Payupki won. The second race began. The boy from Payupki won. He ran against Tikuvi's fastest runners and won every race. When it was over, the men of Payupki collected the things they had won from the men of Tikuvi and carried them

home. They gave some of their winnings to Spider Grandmother, and she was contented.

The chief of Payupki sent for the boy runner. He said,
"Now you must learn to run as you have never run before.
The people of Tikuvi are angry. They will come again with
another challenge, and we must be ready."

The boy worked hard to become a better runner. Each
morning at dawn he went out to run. One day his sister
said to him, "I saw you running today. Your feet are slow."

He replied, "Didn't I win over the runners of Tikuvi?"

She said, "Nevertheless, tomorrow I will show you about
running." And the next day she went with him to the running place.

He said, "Go ahead of me. Stand beyond the large rock
where the cottonwood tree is. I shall start from here."

The girl said, "I do not need to start ahead of you."

He said, "Do as I say. When we start running, go to the
sand hole in the east; then return."

So his sister went ahead to the large rock, and they began. The boy was surprised. Instead of closing the distance
between them, he fell farther behind. When his sister reached
the sand hole, he was still a long way off. She passed him
coming back, saying, "Run, brother, run!" By the time he
made his turn around the sand hole she was far away.
When he was halfway back, she had already finished. He
returned to the village, and there he found his sister busy
grinding corn.

He asked, "Aren't you too tired to grind corn?"

"No," she said. "It was nothing."

Again the next day they went out to run together. This
time they started from the same place. But soon the girl

was far in front. She went around the sand hole and passed her brother going the other way. She taunted him, saying, "Run, brother, run!"

He could not catch her. She finished and went on to the village. He arrived at his house. He saw his sister grinding corn. And he asked her, "Sister, aren't you too tired to do that?"

She said, "No, the running was nothing."

The following day they went again to the running place, and the girl said, "I shall start from here. You go ahead and begin at the large rock where the cottonwood tree is." He went ahead, wondering if even this advantage would help. They began. Before he reached the sand hole, his sister passed him. She left him far behind, finished, and went on to the village.

The boy arrived. He went to the chief's house. He said, "I am not the fastest runner in Payupki. My sister is the fastest." The chief pondered on it.

In time the chief of Tikuvi came again to visit with the chief of Payupki. They sat in the kiva and smoked, and at last the chief of Tikuvi said, "We are having races four days from now. Bring your best runner. He will race against our young men."

The chief of Payupki agreed. "We shall come. But now our best runner is a girl." The chief of Tikuvi listened, they talked, and then he went home to Tikuvi, where he told the people what he had learned.

The night before the race began, the men of Tikuvi went to the kiva to make plans. Because they had been beaten before, they knew that if they were to win this time, they would have to use sorcery. They sent a messenger to get

Spider Grandmother, but he came back without her, saying, "She is not there. Her house is empty. It looks as if
no one lives there now." But they had other people with
knowledge of sorcery, and they devised a plan to win the
contest.

In the kiva at Payupki, also, there was planning. Spider
Grandmother rubbed the legs of the girl runner with her
medicine. She said, "The people of Tikuvi are bad-hearted.
They intend to win the contest by sorcery. So when the
girl runs, I will take on my other form and become a spider.
I will sit on her ear and tell her what to do."

The night passed, and the day of the race came. Everyone gathered at the Tikuvi racing grounds. This time not
only the men of Payupki came, but the women also, because it was a girl who was going to represent the village.
People bet whatever they had brought—moccasins, bows,
belts, turquoise beads, shawls, even pots and grinding stones.
The girl from Payupki tucked her skirt under her belt and
prepared to run. The first race began; it ended. The girl
from Payupki had won. The people of Tikuvi paid their
debt to the people of Payupki. The second race was run.
The Payupki girl finished first. Again the people of Tikuvi
paid their debt to the people of Payupki. The girl won the
third race, and the fourth. By now the people of Tikuvi had
lost everything they had brought to bet on the contest.

It was time for the last race to start. The Payupki men
wanted the betting to go on. The Tikuvi men said, "We have
nothing more." They were sullen. They were ready to leave.

But the Tikuvi women looked at the piles of things the
Payupki people had won. They said, "We want to go on
with the betting. We have no more things to put up. But

we will do it this way. If our runner wins, all those things in the piles will belong to us, the things that were ours and the things that were yours. If your runner wins, all the women of our village will belong to you. We will go to Payupki and become the wives of Payupki men." The men of Tikuvi did not like that. They discussed it. At last, because they planned to use sorcery to win the final race, they decided to take a chance. They felt certain of victory. They agreed. And the people of Payupki also agreed.

So the final race began, and Spider Grandmother changed herself into a spider and sat on the Payupki girl's ear. At first the girl and the boy runner of Tikuvi ran together, neither one ahead and neither one behind. But after a while the girl took the lead. Spider Grandmother urged her on, saying in her ear, "Run, daughter, run!" Suddenly there was a whirring sound, and a white dove flew past them. Spider Grandmother said, "You see what they are doing? They have transformed the boy into a bird." The dove was far ahead when they reached the turning place. So Spider Grandmother called out to a hawk that was sitting on a tall rock on top of the mesa. The hawk swooped down from his place and struck the dove. The dove fell to the ground and fluttered there, while the girl passed him. But after a while they heard the whirring sound again, and once more the dove was in the lead. Again Spider Grandmother called on the hawk to strike, and again it struck and knocked the dove to the ground. The girl with Spider Grandmother on her ear took the lead. When they were almost in sight of the finishing place, the dove passed them for the third time. Once more Spider Grandmother called the hawk. Again it came and struck the dove down. Now the girl runner of Payupki ran swiftly and ended the race. The people of her village applauded her as she finished. But the people of Tikuvi were silent, and the men were sour and angry, for they had lost their women. They spoke black words at their runner when he arrived.

The Payupki people took up all their winnings, they took the Tikuvi women, and they went home and celebrated their victory, not forgetting to give presents to Spider Grandmother. As for the men of Tikuvi, after they got home, they tried to do all the things the women used to do for them, but they did things badly. As time went on, they became more and more angry over what had happened to them. At last they decided to go to Payupki and fight. They made bows; they made arrows; they prepared for battle.

Spider Grandmother heard about the happenings, and she called the people of Payupki to the kiva. She said, "In Tikuvi they are preparing for war. They are busy smoothing their arrows and bending juniper saplings to make bows. They plan to come at night when we are sleeping or when we are inside the kiva. They plan to kill all the men and to take all the women to Tikuvi. In Tikuvi there are many men, while in Payupki there are few. Therefore, there is only one thing to do. We must leave this village and go to another place where we will be safe. I know of such a place in the east, at the edge of flowing water. I will guide you to it."

The people talked it over. They agreed with Spider Grandmother. They prepared to leave at once. As the first gray light of dawn came, the men and boys went out and rounded up all their cattle and horses and placed them in a corral. The women prepared food for them to carry. Spider Grandmother gave directions. "Go east to the wall of the mesa," she said. "Descend by the trail and go on until you reach the deep canyon. Take the cattle through the canyon until you reach the springs. There the cattle may drink. After that continue on for four days. The women will follow you." The men left, driving their cattle ahead of them. They followed Spider Grandmother's directions. They passed the village of Awatovi. They went on and found the watering place in the canyon. They continued the journey to the east.

After the men had left Payupki, the women prepared for their journey. They saved what they could from their houses. They packed food, clothing, pots, and grinding stones. They put the baskets on their backs, bracing them with straps around their foreheads. The loads were very heavy. Spider Grandmother spoke, saying, "With such loads as these we shall never get where we are going. Therefore, something must be left behind." She brought out a large jar and placed it on the ground, saying, "We are going far. We cannot take everything. We must take only what we need. Let us put everything else in this jar." So everything that was not necessary for life was placed in the large jar— their turquoise jewelry also. They sealed the jar and buried it in the ground. Then they started east, following the tracks of the men. Some days later they caught up with the men, who were waiting for them. There they rested in a temporary camp until Spider Grandmother told them it was time to move again.

Once more they went eastward. They had not been traveling long when they saw a stranger coming from the other direction. He also was driving cattle before him. The stranger stopped and spoke to the chief of Payupki, but the chief could not understand him. Spider Grandmother came, she understood all languages, and she listened to the man. "He is a Castilla. He wants to gamble with us."

The chief asked, "What kind of game does he want to play?"

"He has cattle; we have cattle," Spider Grandmother said. "He wants to bet his cattle against ours."

"No," said the chief. "That is not possible. We have come too far to take such a risk. These cattle are all that we have left."

"Unless we gamble," Spider Grandmother said, "he will not let us pass."

"Can he prevent us?"

"Yes," Spider Grandmother answered. "He carries a magic killing stick."

"Very well," the chief said. "Since we have no choice, we will do it. What is the contest?"

The Castilla pointed to a dead tree standing in the distance. Spider Grandmother said, "It is this way: He will shoot his weapon at the tree. One of our men will shoot at the tree. Whoever splits the tree wins the contest."

The chief called the best bowman of Payupki to come forward. He had strong arms and a thick hunting bow. The chief said, "You will compete for us. May your arrow fly straight and hard, for all our cattle depend on it."

The Castilla tried it first. He raised his magic stick and

pointed it at the dead tree. There was a loud noise, and
black smoke came out of the end of the stick; but the tree
remained as it was. Now it was the turn of the Payupki
bowman. Spider Grandmother asked the Payupki chief to
name the best medicine man in the village. The chief named
him, and Spider Grandmother told him to come and stand
with the bowman. He came and stood there. Spider Grandmother instructed him what to do.

As the bowman placed his arrow against the bowstring,
the medicine man called out, "Place your arrow in the
bow!" Instantly a dark storm cloud formed overhead. As
the bowman pulled back his bowstring, the medicine man
called out, "The bow is bent!" And when he said this, the
storm cloud grew larger. As the bowman released the arrow,
the medicine man called out, "The arrow flies!" There was
a loud clap of thunder, and a bolt of lightning came down
from the sky. For a moment the dead tree glowed as though
it were on fire. Then it shattered and fell in many pieces.
The people went to where the tree had stood. They saw
the arrow sticking in a fragment of wood. They looked at
the Castilla. He turned his eyes away, thinking he would
not pay his bet. But he looked again at the shattered tree
and at the dark storm cloud hovering overhead.

At last he said, "You have won. Never before have I
seen such a thing. Take my cattle."

So the people of Payupki took his cattle, and now their
herd was much bigger than before. They went on to the
east. They traveled many days, and they arrived at the
place Spider Grandmother had chosen for them at the edge
of running water. They built a new village there, just
south of a place called Sioki, and they gave it the name of

their old village, Payupki. The old village that they abandoned in fear of the men of Tikuvi—you can still see its ruins. It was built in ancient times, and then it was left behind, and this is the story of how it happened.

—FROM PEOPLE OF THE SHORT BLUE CORN
BY HAROLD COURLANDER

Why Blackbird
Has White Eyes

(NAVAJO)

HOSTEEN CLAH CHEE TOOK A LONG BREATH AND BEGAN. . . .

In the long, very long ago, when the world was new, Mr. Blackbird was not black at all, excepting his eyes, which were so black that they reminded one of two beads of shining jet. At that time this young man went about dressed in a soft feather coat as white as snow. He wore shoes and leggings of fawnskin dyed bright yellow. Altogether he was a very handsome fellow, greatly admired by the girls and women in the valley, especially when he danced and sang at the gay harvest festivals in late October.

But alas! This fine feathered person was both vain and lazy. He never worked in the cornfields or gathered seeds for food. Much of the time he might be found asleep on the soft mats in his grandmother's hogan or in the shade of a piñon tree. But during his waking hours he busied

himself smoothing his white coat, brushing his yellow leggings, and strutting past the dwellings where lived the pret-
tiest maidens. The other men had little good to say of this
vain dandy, who never planted a field, hunted for game, or
followed a war trail.

However, there was one thing in which he excelled. He
could sing. He had listened to the prayer chants of the
medicine men until he had them memorized. He had listened
to the lark, the mockingbird, and the warbler until he could
imitate their songs. When the harvest was being gathered
and the young men spent the long startlit night singing and
dancing, it was he who sang the sweetest songs and led
the most intricate dances.

One day, as he was sitting by the fire in his grandmother's
hogan, sewing the long hairs from an antelope's fetlock onto
his shoes, so that his step would be lighter and swifter, a
stranger lifted the door blanket and stepped inside.

"I bring you an invitation to a ceremony," the stranger
said. "At the time of the full moon in the month of Slender
Wind there will be a fire dance on the Chuska Mountains
just east of Crystal Springs. Runners have been sent to
invite all Navajo, near and far, and also your Pueblo neighbors." Then the messenger was gone.

Blackbird was thrilled at the thought of leading the
dance chant for the many people who would attend the
fire ceremony and at once began planning the costume he
would wear and the songs he would sing. He would need
white feathers from the nest of the heron, and he would
borrow his grandmother's coral beads. All the maidens
would admire him.

"I will sew a new white ruff around the neck of my cloak,"

he told his grandmother, "and put a high crest on my dance bonnet. On my leggings and belt tassels I will sew hundreds of deer toes to tinkle like falling rain as I dance." But he made no move toward collecting the feathers or buying the deer toes he would need.

"Better begin at once!" advised his grandmother, who was well aware of her grandson's lazy ways.

But Blackbird replied, "There is plenty of time! The dance is still many days away." So he lay by the fire, dreaming of the fine appearance he would make at the dance and of the maidens who would gather in groups to watch him and listen to his songs. But he did nothing at all about improving his costume, which had become rather worn and dusty during the harvest dances in early autumn.

Finally, the day before the fire ceremony arrived, and Blackbird was in a great flurry. Hastily he gathered the feathers from the deserted nests of the white goose and the crane. He visited the homes of the hunters to buy deer toes and buckskin thongs with which to decorate his costume. But the little feathers were awkward to handle, and a hole had to be drilled through each deer toe before he could string it on a tassel. He could not see to work by firelight, so he started early the next morning. His work was often interrupted by friends who were on their way to the ceremony and stopped to ask him to accompany them. So the sun had set and night had flung her dark blanket over mountain and valley before he was dressed and ready to start for the dance.

"Oh, my," he thought as he hurried along the mountain trail, "I know I am late, and I am afraid that someone else will be chosen to lead the chanters!" Just then he came in sight of the medicine lodge and the corral of green cedar branches inside of which the huge central fire was thrusting brilliant arms toward the sky. But the brush wall was too high for him to see if the dancing had started. "Grandmother has told me never to look over the top of the cedar corral for fear of becoming blind!" he muttered to himself. "But I must see if anyone is dancing." So he stood on tiptoe and peered over the green wall of the enclosure. One glimpse he had of the great fire and of the spectators gathered around—then two blazing embers hit his face and burned into his eyes. "My eyes, my eyes!!" he screamed as he ran around to the entrance of the corral and into the midst of the startled people.

"What is wrong with your eyes?" they asked as he continued to hop around, moaning and wailing, with his face hidden in his hands.

"They are gone!" he shrieked. "Just look at my face!" But just as he took his hands away from his face, he tripped over a piece of firewood and fell headlong into the fire.

"Quick, quick! Pull him out! Pull him out!" screamed the people. Someone grasped his feet, and he was pulled out with a jerk. The sparks flew all around, and he was not badly burned.

"Look at him! Just look at him!" everyone was gasping in dismay as he stood there with his white coat all covered with soot, and his yellow leggings gray with ashes, and tears streaming from his empty eye sockets. He was indeed a wretched creature, not at all like the gay fellow they had expected to lead the dances. Everyone was sorry for him.

"What can we do to help him?" they asked one another. "And where can we find another youth to lead the dances?"

They gathered around to try to brush off the soot from his beautiful feather coat. But it would not come off. The more they brushed, the blacker it became, so they succeeded only in spreading the black soot over every feather, and since it was magic soot, it never came off!

"His feathers will always be black!" said Medicine Man. "But he need not remain blind. I know the prayers to cure blindness, and in my buckskin bag I have two sacred beads of white shell that will do very well to replace the eyes he has lost." Medicine Man opened his buckskin bag and took out two beads of white shell and placed them in Blackbird's empty eye sockets. Immediately the tears stopped flowing, and he could see as well as ever.

"White eyes are better than no eyes at all!" thought Blackbird as he opened his mouth to thank Medicine Man for his kindness, but not a sound came out. His mouth and tongue had become so badly scorched when he fell into the fire that now he was unable to say a word.

"Something must be done about this, too," everybody agreed.

So Dove flew to Crystal Spring to fill a hollow reed with water. When Dove returned, Medicine Man said to Blackbird, "Open your mouth."

Blackbird obediently opened his mouth, and Medicine Man poured the healing water on his stiff and blackened tongue drop by drop.

Tank! Tank! Tank! Tank! The sound of the dropping water was like the sound of slowly falling rain. And that is the only song Blackbird has been able to sing since that fire dance on the Chuska Mountains.

—From Navajo Bird Tales by Hosteen Clah Chee

The Summer Birds of K'yakime

(ZUNI)

TO'YALLANNE, THE SACRED MOUNTAIN, IS QUITE FLAT ON THE top, and on every side there are cliffs so steep and high that they seem to meet the clouds. Only a few of the very old men know the secret trail that leads up to the shrines of the war gods. And in the days of the ancients there dwelled in the town of K'yakime, which was built at the foot of the great mountain, a Priest of the Bow who had charge of that trail.

Now the priest had a very beautiful daughter, with long black hair and skin the color of honey. She was like some lovely creature of the forest and, as they are, very shy. She would not grind corn with the other maidens of the village, and she never seemed to see the young men when they were dancing. All day long she would sit in her room alone and grind corn or climb to the housetop and watch the sky.

Of course, the people of the village did not know why this was. In the roof of her room there was a little open skylight, and it happened that during a summer shower one of the rain gods, sailing by on a purple cloud, heard her singing:

Oh, my lovely mountain,
To'yallanne, To'yallanne!
High in the sky,
See the rainmakers seated,
See the cloud, the cloud appear!
See the rain, the rain draw near!
Who spoke?—To'yallanne!

The god looked down from the cloud and saw the maiden. He descended in the raindrops and spoke to her. After that she waited by the skylight, and he came again and again. One evening he took her to his people in the clouds, and they were married. But as she was just a maiden and not at all used to the ways of the gods, they thought it best that she live at her father's house in K'yakime, and the god came to her whenever it rained or when the dew fell at night. She was very happy and did not care for the people of her village, whose eyes could not see the god, her husband.

The springtime came to the plains and the hillsides, and the bright flowers covered the ground. A little boy was born in the room with the skylight. As his father was one of the rain gods, he was not like other children. Before he was many days old, he ran about and spoke to his mother. When one month had passed by, he was like a child of six, and he would climb to the housetops and run about the village and out into the fields, hunting birds and small animals. And although he had only little stones with which to kill them, he never failed to bring something back to his mother.

There were always many feathers for the prayer stick, and his old grandfather would place them in his cornfield and take them up to the shrine of the war gods on To'yal-lanne. But it distressed the child to see that the feathers were always dull in color. "Oh, Grandfather," said he, "let us paint the feathers blue, green, red, and yellow like the starflowers." But the old man shook his head and told the boy that it would be wrong to change the plumage of the songsters of the gods.

Another month passed by and the boy grew strong and straight like the young aspens in the mountains. He saw the bows and the arrows that the men carried. He saw, too, that the arrows went more swiftly than the stones he threw. He could always kill small animals with his stones, but he found that he could not kill the large ones.

One night, when he was sitting on the housetop with his mother, he asked her to tell him where to find the wood that the bows were made of and where to gather the sticks for arrows. But she was silent. The boy begged her to tell him. "I will be a great hunter, little mother, and your house will be supplied with meat and you will have soft robes of deerskin, and my grandfather much good medicine."

Finally, she said, "Little son, you cannot find the wood for bows or the sticks for arrows. You are only a child and must wait. There is a great hollow in the rocks where the morning sun shines on the pink cliffs of To'yallanne, and at the bottom of that hollow there is a cave. Around the cave grow the trees out of which bows are made and also the bushes from which arrow shafts are cut. There are so many of these that there would be enough for all the hunters of our people; but the people cannot get them because there is a terrible bear that lives in the cave, and he is so fierce that no one dares go near it."

The boy listened to all that his mother said, and that night he lay awake and thought of the bear and the bow and the arrow shafts. Early the next morning his mother took her water jar and gourd dipper and went down the path to the spring. The boy watched her from the housetop, then quietly and swiftly ran to the river and crawled along the bank until he reached the little valley that leads to the eastern side of To'yallanne. There he climbed up and up until he came to the rocks and the great hollow where the fine yellowwood trees grew. And all around were the straight sprouts needed for the arrow shafts. . . .

The boy looked around. It was so still and so beautiful; surely there could be nothing to harm him here. "I'll just climb a little higher and cut a stick," he thought. And he started to climb into the mouth of the cavern, but his father, the rain god, saw him and from a cloud threw a flash of lightning that closed up the cave.

The boy sat on a rock and blinked. The cloud sailed by, and the cave opened again. The boy did not understand the warning. He got up and took hold of the rocks to pull himself up to the higher level. Another flash of lightning struck the wall above his head. This time he rubbed his eyes as the light almost blinded him. He thought surely a storm was breaking. He jumped and fell right into the cave, landing by the side of the bear, who was sleeping. The huge animal stood up on his hind legs, grabbed the boy, and began to squeeze him.

"Don't squeeze me so hard, it hurts! Don't squeeze me so

hard, and I will give you something very precious."

"What?" said the bear. "What are you saying?"

"Let me go," cried the boy, "and I will give you something more precious than the moon."

The bear held him closer still. "What have you to give me that is more precious than the moon?"

"Wait a minute! I am all out of breath." The boy tried to think of what he could give the bear that was more precious than the moon, for the only really precious thing he had was his mother.

"Did you climb way up here to bring me a present?" asked the bear, as he loosened his hold ever so little.

"No. I climbed up here to get a piece of wood for a bow and sticks for arrows," said the boy. "But I have something at my home that is so beautiful!"

"Tell me at once, or I will crush you," growled the bear.

"It is my mother. She is more beautiful than the moon."

"I will not let you go unless you promise to give her to me," roared the old bear.

"I will," said the boy.

"Then I will give you a present," said the bear. He freed the boy and then walked out among the yellowwood trees. Crack, crack, he broke down a beautiful young tree, gnawed off its ends, and brought it to the boy. Then he gathered a lot of fine, straight sticks for arrows and also gave them to him.

"Do you know how to make a bow, my son?" asked the old bear.

"Not very well," replied the boy.

"Well," said the bear, "I have cut the ends of the yellowwood, and it is about the right length. Now take it home, and shave down the inside until it is thin enough to bend at both ends. Then lay it over the coals of a fire so that it will get hard and dry. That is the way to make a good bow."

"All right," said the boy, and taking the sticks and the piece of yellowwood, he started to climb down.

"Have you forgotten about my present? When shall I come for her?" asked the bear.

"Oh, about sunset tomorrow my mother will be waiting for you."

"I'll be there," said the bear.

So the boy hurried home with his bundle of sticks and his bow stave, and when he saw his mother, he called out, "Just see what I have brought home. And the bear himself is coming tomorrow evening!"

"Oh, foolish boy!" cried his mother. "The bear might have eaten you!"

"But I'm home again, Mother!" And he shouted for joy and rolled in the sand.

All the next day he worked and made his bow. He stripped his arrow shafts and smoothed and straightened them before the fire. He made the points of obsidian, which is very black and hard, and after he had bound them to the ends with sinew and felt their sharpness, he was glad. Then he tied on the feathers, and just as the sun was setting, they were ready, and he put them on the housetop to dry. No sooner had he done this than he heard a growling noise, and the bear stood at the foot of the ladder.

"So you are here," the boy said. "I thought you would never come."

"Is my present ready?" asked the bear.

"Oh, my mother is waiting for you in the house, but first

come and see what a fine bow I have made." And as he said this, the boy picked up the beautiful bow of yellow-wood. The old bear trudged up the ladder to the housetop. He took the long bow from the boy, and he tried it.

Tanggg! sang out the cord.

"It is good," he said. "But let me see your arrows." The boy showed them to the bear.

"What is that black stuff on the ends?" demanded the bear.

"Obsidian," said the boy.

"That is nothing but black coals," said the bear.

"They are good sharp points," said the boy, pretending to be angry.

"You are quite wrong, little boy." And the bear laughed at him in a most unpleasant manner. "Why, they would crumble up if they hit that water jar over there."

"All right then," said the boy. "Just let me try one of those coals on you!" The old bear said it would just blow into ashes, and laughing at the boy, he walked across the roof and stood in the corner.

The boy took one of the arrows and fitted it into the bow. *Tanggg!* sang the bow, and the arrow went straight into the old bear's heart. "*Wah!*" howled the bear, and he gave a great snort, rolled over, and died.

"Ha!" shouted the boy. "Come quickly, Mother, I have killed the bear of To'yallanne."

His mother ran to the top of the house, with her father, the old Priest of the Bow. When they saw the great bear lying there before them, and the child waving his bow in the air, they gave thanks to the Gods of the Universe. "We must plant prayer sticks," said the old grandfather.

"The little one must plant them in the field," said the mother. So the boy, the son of the rainmaker, took the prayer sticks and went to the summer fields all covered with flowers. But no sooner had he come to the field than the sound of fluttering wings came out of the plume offerings. It was the sound of the Sacred Birds of Summerland as they flew away, and because the boy had wished it, the birds' wings had turned blue, green, red, and yellow, too—yellow like the starflowers in the fields.

—FROM ZUÑI INDIAN TALES BY AILEEN NUSBAUM

Plains

T he Native Americans of the Great Plains tribes lived on vast rolling lands stretching west to the Rocky Mountains, south to western Texas, north into the Canadian prairies. It was the homeland of the buffalo, and the tribes followed the herds on horseback, pulling travois, two-poled skin sledges, loaded with portable belongings and hot coals, which they wrapped in buffalo skins. Their tipis were large and painted with geometric designs. Scores of different tribes roved the plains, each speaking its own language but able to communicate with others through a vivid hand-sign vocabulary. The tribes used decorations of fringe, feathers, and beadwork. The buffalo was the staple of their livelihood, and every part of the animal was used for food, shelter, clothing, utensils, or recreation.

When the white man and the advent of the railroads eliminated the buffalo herds, life changed for the Plains people. But the tribes of no other area had such a wealth of recorded history and lore as they had, for lists and diaries, and extensive government reports had preserved the stories and cultural records of the Kiowa, Sioux, Pawnee, Dakota, Cheyenne, Blackfeet, Swampy Cree, and many others.

In Nebraska and Kansas, instead of tipis, the dwellings were often circular earthen lodges, with an entrance to the east and the hearth in the middle. The rounded roof symbolized the sky, and the lodge poles the stars. Stories often centered on the rituals associated with the sun dance, the medicine lodge, or seasonal celebrations, or they related tribal history or hero epics.

But Plains storytellers relished the cycles of tales about the various tribal tricksters, at once both fools and miracle workers. Among the Kiowa he was Saynday; for the Blackfeet, Na'pi; for the Cheyenne, Wihio; for the Cree, Wesukechak; for the Dakota, Iktomi; for the Skidi-Pawnee, Coyote. So vast was the Plains area that it often overlapped the Plateau-Columbia Basin tribal culture and its folklore.

The Cheyenne host on a storytelling night sat at the back of his tipi, with the storyteller at his left. That storyteller ceremonially touched the bowl of his pipe to the earth, chanted a prayer that his words might be true and straightforward, and began. Sessions might last far into the winter night, with occasional pauses for smoking, but when he said, "That cuts it off! Who can tie one to it?" the listeners knew the storytelling had ended for that evening.

Iktomi and the Ducks

(DAKOTA)

IKTOMI IS A SPIDER FAIRY. HE WEARS BROWN DEERSKIN LEG-gings, with long, soft fringes on either side, and beaded moccasins on his feet. His long black hair is parted in the middle and wrapped with red bands. His braids hang over his ears and fall forward on his shoulders.

He paints his funny face with red and yellow and draws black rings around his eyes. He wears a deerskin jacket, embroidered with bright colored beads. Iktomi dresses like a real Dakota brave. In fact, his paint and deerskins are the best part of him. Because Iktomi is a wily fellow, his hands are always in mischief. He prefers to spread a snare rather than to earn the smallest thing by honest hunting. Why, he laughs outright when someone unsuspecting is caught in a trap.

He believes there is no one as clever as he! And so, of course, he cannot find a single friend. No one will help him when he is in trouble. Those who come to admire his handsome beaded jacket and long-fringed leggings soon go away sick and tired of his vain words and mean laughter.

One day he sat alone and hungry in his tipi. Suddenly he rushed out, dragging his blanket after him. He quickly spread it on the ground and began tearing up the dry, tall grass with both hands. Then he tossed it into the blanket. After tying the four corners together in a knot, he threw the bundle of grass over his shoulder.

Snatching up a slender willow stick with his free left hand, he started off with a hop and a leap, bouncing the bundle on his back from side to side. He did not pause for breath until he came to a hilltop. Below him lay a stretch of marshland and a river. He smacked his lips, as if tasting tender meat, as he looked toward the river. "Aha!" he grunted, satisfied with what he saw. A group of wild ducks were dancing and feasting in the marshes. With wings outspread tip to tip, they moved up and down in a large circle. Within the ring, around a small drum, sat the singers, nodding their heads and blinking their eyes.

In unison they sang a merry dance song and beat a lively tattoo on the drum.

On a winding footpath nearby appeared the figure of a brave. He bore a very large bundle on his back. With a willow cane he propped himself up as he staggered along beneath his burden.

"Ho, who is that?" called out a curious old duck, still bobbing up and down in the circular dance. The drummers craned their necks till they strangled their song for a look at the stranger.

"Stay! Show us what is in your blanket!" other voices cried.

"My friends, I do not want to spoil your dance. If you

knew what is in my blanket, you would not want to see. Sing on! Dance on! I must not show you what I carry on my back," continued Iktomi, nudging his sides with his elbows. At this reply the ring broke up, and all the ducks crowded around him.

"We must see what you carry! We want to know what is in your blanket!" they shouted. Some even brushed their wings against the mysterious bundle.

Nudging himself again, wily Iktomi said, "My friends, it is only a pack of songs I carry in my blanket."

"Then let us hear your songs!" cried the curious ducks.

At last Iktomi consented to sing his songs. The ducks flapped their wings together and cried, *Hoye! Hoye!* Iktomi, with great care, laid his bundle on the ground.

"I will build a round straw house first, for I never sing my songs in the open air," he said.

Quickly he bent some green willow poles, planting both ends of each one into the earth. These he covered with reeds and grasses. Soon the straw hut was ready. One by one the fat ducks waddled in through the small opening, which was the only entranceway. Beside the door Iktomi stood smiling, as the ducks, eyeing his bundle of songs, strutted into the hut.

In a strange, low voice Iktomi began to sing his queer old tunes. The ducks sat round-eyed in a circle around him. It was dim in the hut, for Iktomi had covered up the entranceway. All of a sudden he burst into full voice. The startled ducks listened uneasily. These were the words he sang: *"Istokmus wacipo, tuwayatunwanpi kinhan ista nisasapi kta."* ("Get up and dance with closed eyes. He who dares to open his eyes will forever more have red eyes!") The ducks rose. They closed their eyes, and holding their wings close against their sides, they began to dance to the rhythm of Iktomi's song.

Iktomi stopped beating his drum. He sang louder and faster. He seemed to be moving about in the center of the ring. The ducks danced faster. Up and down! Shifting to the right, they hopped around and around in their blind dance.

After a while one of the dancers could keep his eyes closed no longer. It was Skiska who peeked at Iktomi in the center of the circle.

"Oh, oh!" he squawked in terror. "Run! Fly! Iktomi is twisting heads and breaking necks! Run out and fly! Fly!" he cried. The ducks opened their eyes. There beside Iktomi's bag of songs lay half of their flock—flat on their backs.

Out they flew through the entranceway Skiska had forced open as he cried out his alarm. As the ducks soared high into the blue sky, they called to one another, "Oh, your eyes are red—red! And yours are red, too!" For the warning words of Iktomi were magic and had proved true.

"Aha," laughed Iktomi, untying the four corners of his blanket. "I shall not sit in my dwelling hungry anymore." He trudged along homeward with nice fat ducks in his blanket. He left the little straw hut for the rains and winds to pull down.

When he reached his own tipi on the high level lands, Iktomi kindled a large fire out of doors. He planted sharp-pointed stakes around the leaping flames. On each stake he fastened a duck to roast. A few he buried under the ashes to bake. After disappearing within his tipi, he came out again with some huge seashells. These were his dishes.

Placing one under each roasting duck, he muttered, "The sweet fat will taste delicious with the hard-cooked breasts." He heaped more willows on the fire and sat down on the ground with crossed shins. His long chin between his knees pointed toward the red flames while he kept his eyes on the browning ducks. His hands hung just above his ankles, and he clasped and unclasped his long, bony fingers. Now and then he sniffed impatiently at the savory odor.

The crisp wind which stirred the fire also played with a squeaky old tree beside Iktomi's tipi. The tree was swaying from side to side, and it cried in an old man's voice, "Help! I'll break, I'll fall!" Iktomi shrugged his great shoulders but did not take his eyes from the ducks even once. The dripping of amber oil into pearly dishes, drop by drop, pleased his hungry eyes. But the old tree would not stop.

At last Iktomi could stand it no longer. "What is this noise that makes my ear ache!" he exclaimed, holding a hand to his ear. He rose and looked around. The voice came from somewhere in the tree. Iktomi began climbing the tree to find where it came from. Just as he placed his foot on a branch, the wind came rushing by and broke it. Iktomi's foot was caught in the crack.

"Oh, my foot is crushed!" he howled. In vain he pulled and puffed to free himself. As he sat a prisoner in the tree, he saw, through his tears, a pack of gray wolves roaming over the level lands. Waving his hands in their direction, he called in his loudest voice, "Hey! Gray wolves! Don't come here. I'm caught fast in the tree so that my duck feast is getting cold. Don't you come to eat up my meal!"

The leader of the pack, upon hearing Iktomi's words, turned to his comrades and said, "Ah, listen to that foolish fellow! He says he has a duck feast to be eaten! Let us hurry there for our share!" Away bounded the wolves toward Iktomi's lodge.

From the tree Iktomi watched the hungry wolves eat up his nicely browned fat ducks. His foot pained him more and more. He heard the wolves crack the small, round bones with their strong, long teeth and suck out the marrow. *Hin-hin-hin!* sobbed Iktomi. Tears washed brown streaks down his red-painted cheeks. Smacking their lips, the wolves began to leave when Iktomi cried out like a pouting child, "At least you have left my ducks baking under the ashes!"

"Ho! Po!" shouted the mischievous wolves. "He says more ducks are to be found under the ashes! Come, let us have our fill this once!" Running to the dead fire, they dug up the ducks with their paws, raising a cloud of ashes like gray smoke.

Hin-hin-hin! moaned Iktomi when the wolves scampered off. Too late the sturdy breeze returned, and the crack was spread apart. Iktomi was set free, but alas! he had lost his duck feast!

—From Old Indian Legends by Zitkala-Sa

Small Star and the Mud Pony

(PAWNEE)

ON THE BANKS OF A WIDE RIVER THAT RUNS THROUGH THE prairies of western Nebraska there was at one time a village called Fish-Hawk. None of the people in it was wealthy or famous; but their earth lodges were comfortable, corn grew in their fields, buffalo supplied meat, skin hides, cooking utensils, and household articles, and most of the families owned at least one horse.

During the long winters, stories were told around the fires; the women made moccasins, pouches, and shirts fringed, beaded, or decorated with porcupine quills dyed red, blue, yellow, and green. Often the people played with plum stones and baskets or darts. However, when spring and fall came, the women worked planting corn or harvesting it, drying meat and other foods. The men and boys enjoyed ring-and-stick contests or readied their weapons for the summer buffalo hunts. And there were many ceremonials to the great Tirawa, with dancing and feasting.

In one small lodge, however, where Small Star lived with his father and mother, there was little corn and little meat. Worst of all, there were no horses! This made Small Star very unhappy, for he loved horses more than anything. When the other boys took their horses to the river to water them, he sat apart and watched with envy.

One day Small Star decided to build a corral in a hollow across the river. He picked willow boughs and found some rocks, and he made a small gate. Then, when it was finished, he dug a great quantity of mud from the riverbank and brought it to the corral. He filled a buffalo bladder with water from the river and poured it over the mud, making it very sticky. Then, carefully, he began to mold two small ponies from the soft mud, taking great pains with the tails, the hooves and the ears. One little horse he left dun-colored; the other he made sorrel, by mixing in some red clay. He also smoothed some white clay across its face to make a blaze. It was dark when he had finished, and he was too tired to be hungry. When he arrived home, he immediately fell on his sleeping pad and went to sleep without telling his parents anything about his day's work.

Early the next morning he crept from the lodge, crossed the river, and unlatched the corral gate. There stood his two little ponies, their tails out and their heads lifted, almost as though they were breathing after a run. Small Star patted them with delight; then he gathered fresh grass and cottonwood shoots to feed them and spent the rest of the day talking to them as though they could understand his joy in their company. At night he closed the corral carefully, went home, and again told no one of his new ponies.

Every day after that he visited them, fed them, and brought them water to drink. But one morning he saw that the dun pony had dried out and lay crumbled to dust. The bald-faced sorrel still stood. Small Star cried and determined to take special care of the one that remained. After that he spent even more time in the corral, sleeping there at times.

One day a runner came into the village. "The buffalo are returning," he said. "They have been seen in great herds on the plains to the west. It is time to go out for the summer hunting." At once the tipis were brought out and packed, and food and equipment assembled for the hunt. Excitement was everywhere, with children running here and there, dogs barking, and horses trampling and neighing. Small Star's parents looked for him, as they packed their meager belongings, but they could not find him, for he was across the river in the corral with his mud pony. At last they left with the rest of the villagers, thinking he must be with the other children.

When Small Star returned to Fish-Hawk village, he saw only scattered possessions and empty earth lodges—no animals, no people, and no food remained. He felt very lonely and hungry, and he wondered what he should do. He had no idea where the villagers were going, and he knew they moved fast when they went on the summer buffalo hunt. He searched till he found some parched corn and jerky that had been left behind; then he lay down in his empty lodge, feeling lost and frightened. He slept fitfully and in his dreams seemed to be chasing his mud pony around. Then, in his dream, a star rose in the western sky, brilliant and low-hanging, and he heard the voice of Great Tirawa speaking to him: "Small Star, I have seen your grief, and I know how you love your mud pony. I will help you. Go out to him tomorrow, and take care of him." The dream faded, and Small Star awoke; but only the night wind sighed around the lodge. A large star shone in the west, as in his dream, and Small Star slept again, with tears on his cheeks.

The following day he hunted through the village for more

forgotten food, then ran to give his mud pony fresh grass. As he watered him, he kept thinking of the words of Tirawa and the dream, and he wondered what they meant. That night he slept beside his horse, and in his dreams the mud pony spoke to him: "Small Star, little master, do not be afraid, for I am of the earth, and you have fashioned me of the mud from the riverbank. Now Mother Earth has taken pity on you. If you will do as I say, all will go well for you, and someday you will become a great chief."

When morning came, Small Star looked for his mud pony. It was gone! But standing outside the corral and neighing softly was a sorrel horse with a white blaze across its face. The pony was pawing the ground and shaking its mane! Small Star leaped to his feet and ran to it. He felt its shining coat, nuzzled its velvety cheek. "Are you real, beautiful one? Are you indeed my mud pony come alive? Ah, Tirawa, how great, how kind you are! Hear my thanks. I will remember your words and do as you wish!"

Small Star found a rope, put it around his pony's neck, and led him to the river to drink. The pony spoke to him: "I am truly your mud pony! Mother Earth has listened to your heart; you and I will travel to your people now. They are far away, but I know where to go. Lead me to the top of the bank; then mount, and do not direct me, for I know my way."

Small Star could hardly believe his ears, but he did as the pony told him. They traveled on and on, and when night fell, they came to the first site the villagers had used, and again the pony spoke: "Go forage for your food in the camp, for I shall find my own food." So Small Star picked up whatever he could find left behind. He slept the night with his head against the pony's warm flank. The next day, and the next, they did the same thing, each time moving farther out on the great plains, till at noon of the fourth day they found a campsite with coals still warm in the fire pit. Then Small Star knew they would soon catch up with the villagers. And indeed, at sunset they saw their tipis ahead.

Then the mud pony said, "Leave me here and go find your tipi. Waken your mother, for she has grieved for you. When the people break camp tomorrow, stay behind, and I shall be waiting for you to ride."

So Small Star went gladly and, after hunting for the smallest tipi, went in and threw some dried grass on the coals, which spurted up. He wakened his mother gently. "See, I am here! I have come back to you." At first his mother could not believe that he was real, but at last she hugged him and cried over him. Then she prepared food for him, and his parents rejoiced to find him alive and well. In the morning all the relatives and friends came to the tipi to share his parents' happiness. The next day Small Star rose early and went back to where the pony waited. Small Star mounted, and they followed the villagers at a distance.

For several days they continued on in this way. Then the pony spoke again: "My son, it is time for the people to see that you have a horse. The chief will send for it, and he will offer you four horses .for me. Take them. I shall return to you!"

The boy rode his pony proudly into the camp, and everybody pressed around him. "What a fine little horse! How lively, how sturdy! He is just the color of Mother Earth!" They were happy and pleased for Small Star, for they knew how much he loved horses and how poor his parents were.

Word reached the village chief, who came himself to see the pony. He examined it carefully and invited the boy to eat with him in his tipi that night—a great honor for anyone!

Small Star thought to himself, "It is just as the pony told me!" He went and ate in the great chief's tipi, and when the chief told him how pleased he was with the sorrel horse and offered four of his best mounts in exchange, Small Star accepted the offer.

The chief took the pony and set him out to graze, but the pony would not eat. Nevertheless, the chief was satisfied with his new horse and waited eagerly for the coming hunt to try him out. That night the boy was lonely and dreamed of his pony. In his dream the pony said, "Do not mourn, for I shall be back. But take a buffalo hide, and tan it carefully, my son. Be sure that you place it around me each night, to protect me." And so each night Small Star carefully covered the pony with the buffalo hide he had tanned.

Scouts appeared in the camp—a great herd of buffalo was approaching, and many hunters would be needed. At the head, and first into the herd, rode the chief on the sorrel pony. He was proud of the horse's speed and quick response to his leading and his skill in the hunt. When the chief was the first to bring down a buffalo, he was elated! It spurred him to try again and again, and he rode on and on—indeed, he would have taken many more, but suddenly the horse stumbled. Its hind foot was injured and hung disjointedly! The pony was ruined, and the chief was very angry! He returned to the encampment and demanded that Small Star return his four horses. Then, in disgust, he pushed the mud pony toward the boy. Small Star appeared to be very upset, but secretly he was delighted! The chief exclaimed loudly, for all to hear, "Hah! A fine horse! Even though he could run well, he looks just like a mud pony!" From that time on, Small Star's name was changed, and he was called Mud-Pony-Boy.

He took his horse to the outskirts of the camp, and there he worked over him, using herbs and compresses. And before long the foot had healed. The chief wanted to have the pony back; but Mud-Pony-Boy would not agree, and no more was said.

The villagers of Fish-Hawk had moved on to try for more buffalo when suddenly an enemy force appeared on the horizon. The women and children ran to their tipis as the men rode out to war. The pony spoke to Mud-Pony-Boy: "My son, heed my words. Go and coat yourself with mud, the same color as mine. When the warriors shoot at you, their arrows will not pierce the earth covering. Therefore, do not be afraid. Be daring!" Mud-Pony-Boy covered himself with mud and rode out at full speed into the midst of the enemy braves. He unseated an enemy warrior, who turned and fled in fear!

Mud-Pony-Boy rode back to camp in triumph with the other men. They hailed him and said, "Mud-Pony-Boy has become a brave!"

Shortly thereafter the people of Fish-Hawk struck their summer camp and returned to their earth-lodge village on the bank of the great river, far to the east. They had plenty of food and other provisions for winter, and their corn stood waiting to be harvested.

But soon after they had returned, another enemy tribe invaded the village. There were many warriors, and among them was one whose spirit powers were those of Turtle. He was a very great warrior, and Mud-Pony-Boy watched him carefully and soon discovered that the warrior could not be hurt except in one place. Only under his arm could he be fatally wounded. Mud-Pony-Boy wheeled his pony around, and just as the warrior raised his arm to pull his bowstring, Mud-Pony-Boy thrust his sharp, long lance into Turtle Man's armpit and killed him. After that Mud-Pony-Boy took many horses and did many brave deeds. The enemy was routed, and peace returned to Fish-Hawk village. Each night, however, Mud-Pony-Boy was very careful to place the buffalo hide over his beloved pony.

Years passed, and the men met in council. "Mud-Pony-Boy has many times shown himself to be a brave and skillful leader. Our chief is old now. Let him choose Mud-Pony-Boy as his successor, to become chief when the time comes."

The months went by, and one day Mud-Pony-Boy found among his herd of horses a new colt, sorrel-colored with a white blaze on its face. It was the image of his mud pony! That night in his dream his beloved pony spoke to him again: "My son, you have done well. You have proved yourself a true brave and a wise man. You will become a great chief, and people will love you and trust your judgment. My task is finished. I must go back to Mother Earth. Raise the colt, and love it as you have loved me."

That night a storm arose, and when Mud-Pony-Boy took the buffalo hide to cover his horse, he could not find it. He grieved and could not sleep, and early the following morning he crossed the river and went to the corral he had built in his childhood. The sorrel pony lay on the ground, a mound of river mud, with only a dab of white clay where the blaze had once been.

He again heard the voice of his pony: "Do not weep. We were together over many years and have done all that was needed. I have gone back to Mother Earth. You will become a great chief, and your colt will become a great horse, as dear to you as I have been."

Mud-Pony-Boy returned to his village, and he did, indeed, become a great chief, and his colt, a great horse.

—Retold by Dorothy de Wit

Plateau-
California

When Lewis and Clark led their expedition across the Rocky Mountains and into the heart of the West, a Shoshoni woman, Sacajawea, was their guide. Without her knowledge of the territory, they might well have perished. The Plateau area extends from the eastern wall of the Rockies to the Cascade Mountains, from British Columbia in the north, to Nevada in the south. The landscape is marked by dense forests, high mountains, wild rivers, and semidesert. Many nomadic tribes, loosely organized, speaking a multitude of languages, lived there. Cultures varied widely, as did religions and histories, heroes and tricksters. The latter were by turn greedy, sly, foolish, or funny. Each wrought good for his tribe but as often brought trouble on himself. Native American storytellers used their faces and bodies, as well as gestures, to dramatize their tales: Skinkoots (Kutenai or Kootenai), the coyote, Old-Man (Blackfeet), Itsayaya (Nimipoo), Wiskedjak or Blue-Jay, called Whiskey Jack (Canadian Plateau), were all brought vividly to life. The stories often ended with the words: "And the rat's tail fell off!"

Among Californian tribes, the people were more settled, and family groups predominated. Each tribe had its own customs and its own language. Some of the tribes, affected by the Spanish missions, adopted new ways, and language patterns, and even a new religion. Some were later absorbed by the Spanish culture.

Skinkoots Steals
the Springtime

(KOOTENAI)

IN THE DAYS OF SKINKOOTS, THE COYOTE, THE WINTERS WERE
twelve months long and very cold. The great river Kootenai
was bound in ice, and the North Wind buried the villages
deep in snow so that even the hunters could not leave their
tipis, and no game crossed the valleys.

In a village far north on the river, the seasons were kept
hanging in a tipi, each in a great mooseskin bag. At the end
of twelve months of cold, the keeper, who was an old
woman, would in turn untie the hide bags which contained
the springtime, the summer, and the fall, and for a brief
time each season would be allowed out into the world.
Then they would be tied up again in their skin bags and
hung in the great tent, and winter, with its icy winds and
deep snow, would reign again for another twelve months.

In one of the villages there lived an old woman. She
lived by herself, for all her sons were gone. During the short

summer she picked berries and dried them, plucked and
stored the rose hips, gathered nuts, and made pemmican.
But now she had used up most of her foods. So when
Skinkoots came to her tent and asked for something to eat,
she had little to give him. She cried when he gobbled it all
down! "The winter will last a long time yet, Skinkoots! You
have eaten the last of my food, and I shall go hungry! What
am I to do? There is no more food anywhere."

"Have I indeed eaten all your food, Squirrel Woman?
Well then, you must cry—cry loud and long and wail till the
villagers run to see what has happened!" replied Skinkoots.

"Why should I weep so loudly? I am old and alone, and
I have taken care of myself many winters, Skinkoots. It is
you who have brought this trouble on me! *Aaaaaaiiiiii*—what
am I going to do?"

"Cry!" answered Skinkoots. "Only cry very loud. All the
people will hear you. They will come running through the
cold to your tent to see what is wrong. Cry, Squirrel Woman,
and do not say anything at all. Cry and cry, and I will take
care of everything."

So Squirrel Woman huddled in her blanket close to the
small fire, and she began to weep and wail very loudly. One
after another the villagers came to her tent and asked
her, "Why do you cry? What is wrong?" But she would not
reply, just kept on crying. Then Skinkoots stood up.

"Did you say you have no more food, Squirrel Woman?"

"Yes," she replied.

The villagers looked at each other and said, "We must
do something to make spring come sooner."

"There is only one thing to do," said Skinkoots. "We must
steal the springtime." And everybody agreed.

But now, who should be chosen to steal the springtime? Skinkoots, of course, would go, but he would need help, so many of the men said that they would go with him. "But we will need someone who can go into the tent without the old woman hearing him," they said, "someone who can walk on silent feet and is both daring and quick!" Each man looked at the other, and finally a boy called Lynx came forward.

"I can walk secretly, and I am not afraid," he said.

"Well," said Skinkoots, "we will try then. We will do it this way. We will go north till we come to the hill on the edge of the prairie from which one can see the tent with the seasons. We will need a strong person to stand on that hill because he must catch the bag when I throw it to him and run away fast. And as he runs, he must tear the hide apart and let out the springtime!"

Again the people looked at each other. "That one," they said at last, and they chose Grizzly Bear, strongest of them all, with sharp, long claws.

All the people, led by Skinkoots, followed the Kootenai River north, stomping through snowdrifts, pulling their blankets tightly around them against the bitter wind. When at last they reached the hill, Grizzly Bear and the villagers stayed behind. Lynx and Skinkoots ran on to the big tent that held the seasons. Before they arrived, Skinkoots said, "I will wait outside the entrance to catch the bag when you throw it out. Now you must summon your own Manitou to give you special powers. Go into the tent where the old woman guards the bags. But first gather some gum from the pine trees. When you get inside, stand with your back to the fire and your hands behind you so that the warmth of the fire will soften the gum. Ask the old woman to point out the bag with the springtime, and make sure you don't take the wrong bag by mistake! When she turns to point out the bag, grab her from behind, and paste the sticky gum over her mouth so that she cannot call out and rouse the village. Then throw the bag out of the tent to me. I will run with it and then throw it as far as I can to Grizzly Bear on the hill. Do you understand, Lynx?" Lynx nodded to Skinkoots.

Lynx crept into the tent on noiseless feet. As soon as he had located the bags, he moved to the fire; then he turned his back to it, clutching the resin in his hand. The old woman saw him, but he looked cold, a stranger who needed help, and she said nothing. After a while Lynx said, "I have heard that you guard the seasons, old mother. Can you tell me which of these bags holds the autumn?" The old woman pointed to a bag high in the tent. "And which holds summer, old mother, and springtime? Is springtime the farthest one hanging there?" The old woman rose and nodded. Suddenly Lynx grabbed her from behind and covered her mouth with the sticky gum. He held her tightly for a moment, then pushed her aside, leaped up, and, after grabbing the bag, threw it hard out the tent opening. He followed it, and the woman ran out after him, trying to shout for help. But though the villagers saw her waving her arms and pointing, they heard no sound, for the gum kept her mouth tightly closed. By the time they got to her tent and realized what had happened Skinkoots had run quite a distance, with Lynx behind him. The villagers were on his heels; they were gaining ground when Skinkoots raised his arms and threw the bag to Grizzly Bear, who caught it and was on his way. When the villagers reached the hill, Grizzly

Bear and the others were a long way off. The villagers, seeing the chase was hopeless, returned to their homes.

As he ran, Grizzly Bear raked the bag open with his sharp claws. Warm winds sifted out across the earth and began to melt the snow. Sunlight splashed over the trees, and the fragrance of growing plants wafted through the air. By the time Grizzly Bear and Skinkoots and Lynx reached the river the ice was melting, the meadows were greening, and new flowers poked up their heads. The springtime had come! And summer would follow. For months it would be warm. And so it has been, ever since the old woman cried for food and Skinkoots stole the springtime!

—RETOLD BY DOROTHY DE WIT

What Happened to Six Wives Who Ate Onions

(MONO)

THE WESTERN MONO INDIANS LIVED HIGH UP ON THE KINGS River. They knew how to use magic. Here is a story they told:

Once there were six pretty wives. These wives had six husbands who were mountain lion hunters.

One day, while the husbands were out hunting, the wives

went up the mountain to pick clover for food. That day one wife discovered something new to eat—wild onions.

"Yum, these new plants taste better than anything I've ever eaten!" she told the others. "Just taste this." The other wives all tasted the onions. They liked them, too. They ate and ate and smacked their lips and then went home to cook supper for their husbands.

Just as dusk was falling, the husbands came plodding home. Each had killed a big mountain lion.

"Phew! What's that odor?" the husbands asked their wives when they reached their huts. They soon discovered the terrible odor was on the breath of their wives!

"We found this new plant to eat—just taste it," the wives said, and offered some to the husbands.

"No!" they cried in disgust. "Your breath is enough for us—horrible!" They wouldn't even taste the onions. That night the husbands made their wives stay outdoors because the odor of the onions kept them awake. It was cold outside, and the wives didn't like staying outdoors.

The next day, when the husbands had gone hunting, the wives went back to where the onions grew and ate more than they had the day before. Those onions were so tasty they just couldn't help eating them.

When the husbands came home for supper, not one of them had slain a mountain lion. Never before had they come home without mountain lions, and they were very sad.

"The mountain lions smelled that horrible odor on us," they grumbled. "The mountain lions smelled us and ran away fast before we could get near enough to catch them." The wives didn't believe their husbands and said so.

But when the husbands smelled the odor of onions stronger than ever, they scolded. "You can't come near us! You are worse than skunks!"

Again they wouldn't let their wives come inside the huts to sleep. They wouldn't put food out for their wives to eat. The wives went home to their fathers and mothers, but that didn't do any good. They were sent right back to their husbands.

This lasted six days. Each night the men came home without mountain lions, and each night they found their wives had been eating onions again. Finally, what with the strong odor of onions and not getting mountain lions, the husbands went into a terrible rage.

"Go away!" they shouted. "Go away! We can't hunt! We can't sleep nights because you eat so many onions. We don't want you anymore. Go away!"

The next morning, when the husbands had gone, the wives all went up the mountain to where onions grew. Each of them took her magic rope, made of eagle's down. They were hungry, and they were tired of sleeping outside in the cold.

"Let's leave our husbands forever," one wife said. "Our husbands don't like us anymore." They all agreed.

So they climbed and climbed up a big rock. Each wife carried her eagle-down rope. One wife brought her little girl with her. And at last they reached the very top of the rock. They rested awhile. Then the leader of the wives said, "Now is the time for magic. Do you still want to leave your husbands forever?"

"Yes!" they all cried.

So the leader of the wives said a magic word and threw

her eagle-down rope up into the sky. Whoosh! it went, straight up. The center of the rope caught on a piece of the sky so that both ends of the rope hung down to the rock. The women tied all their ropes to the two ends of rope hanging from the sky. The opposite ends they spread out on the rock. Then they clasped hands and called, "Eagle-down ropes, magic ropes, help us!"

They stood on the rope ends spread out on the rock and began to sing a magic song. Then the ropes slowly began to rise and swing around and around, the way a buzzard flies. As the wives sang louder, the ropes made bigger and bigger circles in the sky. Soon the women standing on the ropes were sailing through the sky over the village where they lived.

Their fathers and mothers looked up and saw them in the sky. The people of the village pointed up at them and were very excited. The women in the sky saw their mothers and fathers and their mothers-in-law and fathers-in-law rush into their huts. Next, they saw them come out with food and beads and belts and place all these things on the ground.

"Come back!" the women's relatives cried up to them. "Come back and see what we have for you!" But the women stayed in the sky.

And down below, the husbands looked up and saw their wives. "Why didn't you keep an eye on them?" they scolded their wives' parents. "Why did you let them get away when we were out hunting?"

Now that the wives were gone, the husbands wanted them back. They were lonesome and sad. They got together and tried to think what to do. They decided to use their own magic eagle-down ropes and go up into the sky after their wives. They climbed the rock, sent up their ropes, and sang in the same way their wives had done. Soon they were sailing in the sky over the village.

The old people came out and begged their sons to come back; but the sons wanted their wives, so they kept on singing and going higher and higher into the sky. By this time the wives were very high in the sky since they had had a head start on the husbands. They looked down and saw their husbands coming after them.

"Shall we let them catch us?" they asked each other.

"No," said one. "Our husbands said they didn't want us anymore. Don't let them catch us ever." And they all agreed they would rather be alone in the sky.

As soon as the husbands got closer, the women shouted, "Stay where you are!" The wives had stronger magic in their eagle-down ropes. The men had to stay right where they were below their wives.

They all turned into stars in the place in the sky where they are to this day. The six women are the Pleiades, and are known as the Young Women. The six husbands are called Taurus, and are known as the Young Men.

Whatever the names, there they are, swinging slowly across the sky on clear nights, and all because the women loved to eat wild onions more than anything else.

—FROM STORIES CALIFORNIA INDIANS TOLD
BY ANNE B. FISHER

Coyote and the Swallowing Monster

(NIMIPOO)

WESTWARD THROUGH THE COUNTRY WE NOW CALL IDAHO WENT Itsayaya, the coyote. He was on his way to build a fish ladder on the Salmon River so that the salmon could go upstream to spawn. The people were hungry, and the salmon fishing was difficult. Suddenly he heard the meadowlark calling to him noisily, "Itsayaya, it is no use to build a fish ladder now! All the people are gone."

"Gone?" said Coyote. "Then I will stop my work because I was doing it for them. But where have they gone, sister?"

"The monster has swallowed them all, Itsayaya. Not one remains! The monster, who stretches across these mountains and ends nobody knows where. . . . Oh! He is terrible!"

"I have heard of that monster. They tell me if I go to Kamiah, I will find his head. Perhaps that is where I will go now." Itsayaya went through the Salmon River country, but he saw nobody anywhere. Along the way, he made five knives of stone and a flint fire-making set. These, with a lump of pitch, he strapped to his back. Then he bathed in the swift river, saying, "If I am to be the monster's dinner, I should at least be well washed."

Itsayaya found clay, and he painted himself to match

the grasses and the ridges; then he made a headdress of feathery weeds and a breastplate of bunched grasses. When he approached Kamiah, he tied himself with wild grapevines to three separate peaks. Then cautiously he crept along to the top of the mountain. He looked over the ridge —and there was the monster!

Itsayaya had never seen anything like him. His body was so enormous it spread over the hills and the valleys and disappeared into the horizon. Its eyes were like two round lakes. Coyote crawled into the grass, where the monster could not see him. Then, though his courage was running out fast, he called, "Monster, I have come to swallow you!" The immense eyes roved here and there, trying to locate the voice, but the grasses hid Itsayaya. A second time Coyote mocked his enemy: "I shall draw you in with my great breath, Kamiah Monster!"

This time, the grass around Coyote swayed, and the monster spotted him. "Hah! It is Coyote. I should have known! Come, Itsayaya, swallow me!"

Coyote swelled his chest and took a deep, noisy breath, but the monster hardly flickered his eyelids. Then the monster drew in his breath, and the suction broke one of the grapevines that protected Coyote. Again the monster inhaled, and the second grapevine broke. Itsayaya was almost pulled into the gaping mouth. The monster gulped in a third great breath, and into the cavern of its mouth went Coyote! He just had time to cut the last grapevine now entangled around his feet before he was swallowed. Down, down, down he tumbled, into the long, dark throat. He shivered as he rolled over many bones. When he stopped rolling, he found himself staring at Grizzly Bear, who also had been

swallowed whole. "So Coyote, too, has met the monster."
Grizzly Bear laughed. "I see that all your tricks could not
save you!"

"Nor did your great strength save you, Grizzly Bear!"
retorted Coyote. He pushed the bottom of his foot into
Grizzly Bear's face, and to this day the grizzly bear has a
black snout.

Itsayaya bounced to his feet and moved on cautiously,
but he stepped on Rattlesnake, who hissed angrily, "Hah,
Itsayaya, the clever! Look where you are now!"

"Look yourself, rattler! What use was your poison fang
to you? You'll have a flat head to remember this by," and
Itsayaya jumped on the rattlesnake's head and flattened it.
He continued on until he heard a loud thumping, like a big,
big drum, and he knew he was nearing the monster's heart.
Everywhere he saw terrified men and women, and children, too, crouching together and waiting, waiting. . . .
"For what?" thought Coyote to himself. "They will die, as
I must, unless—" Suddenly he had an idea. He said to some
young boys, "Run quickly to the monster's mouth, and see if
you can pick up some sticks—you must be fast and clever!"

Then he ordered the others, "Stop wailing and listen to
me. Gather up all the bones of those who have already died,
and pile them up in the monster's jaws. He is very stupid,
but do it carefully and make no noise." A short distance
ahead of him, Itsayaya saw something bobbing up and
down. It was the monster's heart.

Itsayaya took out one of his stone knives. Swiftly he began to cut through the heart's ropelike tendons. He felt the
monster shift a little, then settle down again. When the boys
returned with the sticks, Itsayaya took his flints and started

a fire, just under the monster's heart. At first, it burned slowly. Coyote kept sawing away at the tendons, and just as the first one broke, a puff of smoke rose and floated up to the monster's throat. He coughed and choked, and called out in a terrible voice, "Hah! Itsayaya, what are you doing down there? I knew I should not have eaten anyone as evil as you! Get out now, at once—I want to be rid of you!"

But Itsayaya answered by stoking his fire so that it burned higher. And he continued cutting away with his stone knife. A second tendon broke! Then a third, and a fourth. His knives wore out one by one, and he had only one good knife left. The monster was writhing and twisting now and trying very hard to blow Coyote out of himself. His heart thumped more and more slowly.

"Go forward now, all of you--move quickly," Coyote commanded the people. Men and women pushed toward the monster's open mouth. Suddenly as Coyote lashed at it, the monster's heart crashed down. The Kamiah monster lurched wildly and then lay still. The huge creature was dead. The people stumbled out, faint with hunger and dazed by the bright sun. Then they remembered what Itsayaya had said concerning the bones of those who had died, and they placed them on the ground in proper order. Coyote came out last of all. He dipped his hands into the river and sprinkled water over the bones. Wonderful to behold—the dead regained their former shapes and came back to life. They thanked Itsayaya for rescuing them and returned home.

Then Itsayaya turned to the monster's carcass. He cut up the body and threw the parts over the land. To the north he threw the legs. That is why the Blackfeet Indians are tall. The Crow received the head. That is why they have such long hair. To the Coeur d'Alene went the heart, and they are known for their courage. The Nez Percé got the ribs, and they are large of body. The knife Itsayaya threw over his shoulder. It landed far to the north among the Thompson people, who ever since have been famed as hunters.

Then Itsayaya started on his way again. But the Salmon River people stopped him. "How about us, Itsayaya?" they asked. "Have you nothing left for us who live here?"

"Ah," replied Coyote. "Have I indeed forgotten those around me?" He sprinkled drops of blood over the ground. "This will be the land of the Nimipoo. They will be few in number but very brave!"

Ever since it has been as Itsayaya decreed long ago. And to this day the shape of the huge Kamiah monster can still be seen imprinted where he once lay along the Salmon River in western Idaho.

—Retold by Dorothy de Wit

Cottontail Plays a Trick on Coyote

(SIA)

COTTONTAIL SAT IN FRONT OF HIS LITTLE HOUSE, SINGING TO himself in the hot sun:

> A secret I have—a secret is mine,
> A secret so great—a secret so fine!

He raised his long ears and listened and sniffed the piñon gum as it oozed from the trees in the heat. When he heard footsteps, he sang again loudly:

> A secret I have—a secret is mine,
> A secret so great—a secret so fine!

Coyote heard him and crept up softly behind the house. Then when Cottontail opened his mouth to sing again, Coyote sprang on him and held him fast!

"Ohhhhhh!" said Cottontail. "Ohhhhh! Please, Coyote, do not eat me! Listen, I have a secret to tell you. . . ."

"I have a secret to tell *you*, Cottontail!" said Coyote. "You have played your last trick on me! I am going to eat you in a minute! How will you like *that?*" And he smacked his lips and clicked his sharp teeth.

"Oh, please, Coyote, wait a little. I have something to tell you—something you want to hear. It's very important! Please wait, Coyote." Cottontail cringed as Coyote grasped his foreleg more tightly.

"Well then, tell me." And Coyote bent his head lower. "I am waiting, my ears are ready!"

"Ah, I am afraid of you when you are so close, Coyote! The words run out of my head! Let me sit just there at the door of my house again for a moment; then I will be able to tell you!" He rolled his eyes and shivered.

So Coyote took him to the door of his own house, but he remained close to him, and he glared at Cottontail with his red eyes.

"Ah, do not look at me like that, Coyote. My heart thuds so fast that I forgot what I want to tell you."

"I am getting very hungry, Cottontail! Tell me this secret very quickly!"

"Listen, then," and Cottontail swallowed hard and almost whispered. "I am *afraid* . . . I am very, very afraid, for I am so weak and small! When all the people pass me with their bows and arrows, they stare as though they wanted to shoot me right then and there. Oh, how I shake and tremble!" Cottontail began to shake and tremble violently, so that Coyote's paw slipped off his leg, and Coyote was put off his guard! Quick as a flash, Cottontail darted away! Like the wind he ran, and as he ran, he sang:

A secret I have—a secret is mine,
A secret so great—a secret so fine!

Coyote blinked, pulled himself together, and began to

chase Cottontail, but when he had almost reached him, Cottontail dodged into a friend's burrow. The burrow was made of rocks. Coyote was left with a wisp of fur in his claws. Coyote pushed his head into the burrow, stretched out his forelegs to reach for Cottontail, and found nothing! Coyote became very angry— first at Cottontail because he had escaped him again and then at himself. "Stupid, stupid Coyote! Why did I allow that cottontail to fool me with his tricky words? I'll get him someday. But how can I break into a stone burrow?" He pushed and pulled; but his paws were not strong enough to get the rocks apart, and he did not know what to do next.

Cottontail called out to him. "Coyote, here I am in this burrow. Can you kill me now?"

"I cannot move the stones to get you, Cottontail. But you wait! When I build a fire at your door, you won't be singing anymore."

"Where is your wood, Coyote?"

"I do not need wood; there is dry grass all around. It will be fine for my fire!" answered Coyote.

"The grass is my friend and my food, Coyote. Why would it want to kill me?"

"Then I will pull off some piñon boughs and stuff your doorway full. When I light the fire, you won't be able to fool me again!"

"The piñon trees know me well." Cottontail laughed. "I chew on their needles, and eat their nuts, and sit under their branches in the moonlight. They would not burn a friend!"

"Hah! Then I will bring a lump of piñon gum and set fire to it! Sly Cottontail, you do not eat *that*, I know!"

"You are right, Coyote. I am afraid of that. Now I tremble with fear."

Coyote laughed with glee, thinking he had at last discovered a way to make a tasty meal of Cottontail. He gathered up a lump of resin and shoved it into the entrance of the burrow. He made sparks and set fire to the resin. The gum began to melt, and the black smoke rose high and higher. Cottontail began to wail, "Ahhhhh, now it has come! I will surely die this time!"

Coyote danced about and licked his chops.

"The fire is coming in," Cottontail called out.

"Blow on it," said Coyote, laughing. "Blow hard, and blow it out!" As he said it, he sidled up to the entrance and blew a mighty gust into the flames himself.

"Oh, oh, oh!" Cottontail coughed. "The fire is hot! The smoke is very strong! I can see your big red mouth blowing the fire at me. . . ." Cottontail wept. Coyote continued to blow as hard as he could, bringing his muzzle closer and closer to the fire. Suddenly Cottontail poked the hot, sticky gum right into Coyote's face. The hot gum stuck to his eyes, to his fur, to his black nose, to his sharp teeth. . . .

And while Coyote was shrieking and clawing at the gum to get it off, Cottontail quickly slipped out of the entrance and disappeared! Only his song hung in the air behind him.

> A secret I have—a secret is mine,
> A secret so great—a secret so fine!

Coyote made his way sadly home with painful eyes and piñon gum all over him, and he never did discover Cottontail's secret.

—RETOLD BY DOROTHY DE WIT

Pacific
Northwest

Huge twisted cedar logs strewn along the North Pacific shore and on the islands around Vancouver Island and the Olympic Peninsula even today suggest the importance of the cedar tree to those Native Americans living on the coast of southern Alaska as far south as the California border and north to the Queen Charlotte Islands. Here many tribes lived, each with its own language and culture. What they had in common, however, was the use of the cedar for canoes, houses, totem poles; the importance of the salmon in their economy; and the use of eagle down, seal fur, and abalone shell in their arts and celebrations.

Though the details might differ, in general, the Pacific tribes believed that they were descended from a supernaturally born child found drifting on a kelp bed, who was then adopted by a chief, to be reared as his son.

The Nootka and Haida were rich and very skillful seamen. Their enormous carved cedar canoes held several score of men, and they ventured far out into the Pacific waters whale hunting. Their cedar houses were made with great planks, and in front of them stood carved cedar totem poles which told the family history. Such story poles also served as burial monuments that recorded the deeds of the family. This was very important, for among the Pacific peoples there was a strong class distinction—first came the royal chiefs and the princes of the royal families; then the common members of the village; and finally, the slaves captured on raids. The figures of Hawk, Bear, Raven, Killer Whale, Beaver, Eagle, and Wolf are frequently present in the legends.

The trickster of the Tsimshian, Tlingit, Kwakiutl, and Haida tribes was Raven-Who-Set-Things-Right, and it was he who shifted his shape from beak and feathers to human form. He was credited with stealing the daylight, procuring fire, producing water to drink, and creating the salmon.

The same foolish, greedy, tricky culture hero of the Pacific tribes was known as Mink in the Canadian Georgian Bay area, and along the Washington-Oregon coastal inlands, he was Blue-Jay. Whole cycles of tales revolve around these three tricksters.

The Feast of the Mountain Goats

(TSIMSHIAN)

On the upper Skeena River in an area called Prairie Town, there was once a Tsimshian village. Over it towered great mountains, where mountain goats could often be seen leaping from crag to crag. Many hunters lived in the village, and when the harvest moon hung low and the trees turned to gold, they went to the hills to hunt for goats so that the villagers would be provided with food and skin for the winter.

Among the hunters were six brothers, so skillful and daring that they brought down many goats each year. But they ignored the ancient laws and brought back to the village only the kidneys and some of the goat fat. The flesh, the bones, and the skins they left on the mountain slopes for the vultures.

In the same village there lived another young man who was called Black Raven Feather. He had grown up with the old laws: "Kill what is needed, but no more; burn the bones of the animals so that their spirits may be freed; and never take a young kid from its mother." Black Raven Feather burned within when he saw the hunters defy these laws, especially in the spring, when they hunted in the season of the young kids.

One morning early, Black Raven Feather heard cries and shrieks, mingled with the thin bleating of a young goat. The hunters had brought home a kid and given it to the village children for a plaything. The children chased the kid, teased it, and finally threw it into the river. Too young to swim well, too weak to try for the shore, it sputtered and gasped for breath while the children screamed with laughter. The water at that time of year was icy, and the young kid shivered with cold. Pretending pity, the children built a fire on the shore. They dragged the kid out of the water and pushed it so close to the fire that its coat was scorched and its skin burned. Then they dragged it back to the water to cool it off.

Black Raven Feather heard the noise and the terrified bleating of the kid. He raced toward the scene, snatched the goat from the children, and took it home. Gently he wiped away the ashes, the singed hair, and put cool mud on the burned flesh. Slowly the kid stopped shuddering, and at last it fell asleep.

When it wakened, Black Raven Feather fed it and spoke to it. And after a few days, when the goat could walk again, he took it to the foot of the mountains and set it free. He waited until he heard the bleating of the mother goat and the kid's answering call.

The hunters and the children jeered at him. They called

him "woman's heart" and "foolish one!" But he went his way and did not reply. The children soon forgot the kid, and the hunters went back to their hunting. But Black Raven Feather did not forget, and he could not forgive what they had done.

Spring turned to summer. The hot, long days faded, and another autumn painted the hills. One day strangers from the mountains came to the village. Visitors such as these were not common, and the chiefs invited them into their lodge, and celebrated their arrival with feasting and ceremony. The strangers had come with an invitation. A feast was to be held at the foot of the mountain, and the chiefs and the entire village—men, women, and children—were invited. The mountain people had planned a great celebration in their honor. There was excitement everywhere, and the villagers were soon ready to leave.

They traveled all day and toward evening came to a magnificent new lodge, quite unlike their own simple council house. There were many mountain people there to greet them. Then the chiefs appeared. They wore masks carved to look like the heads of mountain goats. They were dressed in jewelry, feathers, and long coats made of goatskins, and their blankets were decorated with strange symbols. The villagers were amazed at such wealth, and they were overwhelmed by the pomp and the ceremony. Dancing, chanting, singing, the chiefs led them into the huge new lodge. One of the young men drew Black Raven Feather aside and guided him to a seat at the rear of the lodge, behind a great post. "We will sit here for the feast, my friend," he said.

The chiefs danced, one after the other, in their strange

goat masks. The chants and the singing grew louder and wilder. At last a dance began, accompanied by a special song which was chanted loudly:

Ah, yi yi, yi, yea haa!
He comes, Prince of the Goats,
He comes, Prince of the Mountain Goats,
His hoof is on the mountain,
He leaps, he springs, he kicks his hooves,
Prince of the Mountain Goats, he comes!
Ah, yi yi, yi, yea haa!

And suddenly, galloping down the mountain side, came an enormous one-horned goat—not a dancer in a mask, but a real animal, which leaped toward the front of the lodge with tremendous strength. His hooves pointed, he kicked against the carved posts—now on one side, now on the other—till the timber groaned and cracked, the posts caved in, and the floor was wrenched loose. With a mighty crash, the lodge collapsed, hurling men, women, children, dancers, and timbers down, down the mountain into an opening abyss! Only Black Raven Feather was left behind, clinging to the lodge post, his face gray with terror. As he clung to it, the post became a slender spruce tree. Below him great boulders tumbled down, and the mountains loomed black all around him as night fell. He was rigid with fear, and could scarcely turn his head, when he heard the voice of his mountain friend. "Do not be afraid! I am here with you. Sleep now, and in the morning I will show you the way to go down safely." And with that, he lay down by the spruce tree and slept. But Black Raven Feather could not sleep. His eyes still saw the crashing lodge, his ears still heard the screams of terror, and he wept!

In the morning his friend said, "Do you understand why this has happened? It is because for years your hunters have slain the mountain goats. Your hunters have grown cruel and careless of the ancient laws. The bones of my people are strewn over the mountains, and vultures feast on their flesh. Only you remembered. I was the young kid you saved from the river and the fire. My people are the mountain goats. They have suffered at the hands of your people and now they are revenged."

Black Raven Feather looked down into the chasm and shuddered. How could he scale those steep rocks? And where should he go, now that his relatives and his village were gone? The mountain goat youth read his fears. "Take my blanket," he said. "When you are safely down, hang it on a tree. And now, do as I say, and you will descend in safety." Then he hung his blanket over the shoulders of Black Raven Feather. As soon as he did so, Black Raven Feather became a young mountain goat. From one rock to another he leaped, calling in a strange bleating rhythm, "On the thumb—left! On the sand—right!," each time balancing in time to his words.

Bleating and jumping—left, right, left, right—he felt the power of the surefooted mountain goat. At last he reached the prairie. He took off the blanket and hung it on a tree branch and was again himself. It seemed to him he heard his friend saying, "Gather the bones of your dead relatives, and arrange them in proper order. Do this for each relative you wish to see. Then jump over them four times—they will revive, and together you can start life again."

Black Raven Feather searched for his family. He gathered their bones and arranged them as they should be, and then, with a prayer in his heart to the mountain spirits, he jumped carefully over them four times. Before his eyes they arose, alive and well.

The following day Black Raven Feather and his family returned to the mountains. They searched long and carefully, gathering the bones of goats wherever they found them. Then they lighted a great fire and burned the bones so that the spirits of the goats would be released and be free again to roam the mountain peaks.

Black Raven Feather and his family built a new village where the ancient laws were always observed. And high on the mountain they often saw the figure of the one-horned mountain goat, wild, erect, and free!

—Retold by Dorothy de Wit

Raven and the Nose of the Gonaqadet

(PACIFIC COAST)

RAVEN WAS HUNGRY AGAIN, HUNGRIER THAN HE HAD EVER been before, and he was always hungry! His hunger was almost unbearable! He flew through the forest, with its trees reaching up and up, and out onto the shores of the Pacific, where the waves might wash up something to eat. From an uprooted cedar tree, he watched the crashing breakers for a while. Far out, he saw the waters twist and suck, in a little whirlpool, and he nodded knowingly. "It is the Gon-aqadet—the monster who lives at the bottom of the sea! How terrible his sharp, strong teeth! How cruel his claws of copper!" Raven shivered at the very thought of meeting him; then hunger clutched at him again, and he turned to look up and down the long shoreline. He must find food, or he would perish! His sharp black eyes spied a point of land, and he saw figures coming and going. He changed into his human form and walked briskly to the village of Kundji. The figures he had seen were the fishermen.

As he came closer, he saw many canoes with their high carved prows floating near the shore, and many more pulled up on land. The fishermen were shouting back and forth, and Raven's searching eyes caught sight of the small boxes stuffed with salmon roe that they would use as bait, for the men were setting out to fish for flounder. Raven's mouth watered, and a cunning thought entered his mind: "Why should such delicious food be wasted as flounder bait?" He pulled his raven beak down and flew up as a bird to wait for the men to push out into the bay. As soon as he saw them drop their lines, he flew out over the water and dived in, changing to a flounder. Slyly he nibbled the salmon roe from each hook. The fishermen felt the pull and drew in their lines, but when they saw that there were no fish and the bait had been taken, they were angry. Again they baited their lines, and again Raven stole the roe. It happened many times, and each time the men became angrier. Finally,

Raven had had enough. He flew back to shore and changed into his human form, in time to meet the fishermen, who were coming back. "It looks as though you've had bad luck today," he said. "I am surprised, for the fish are leaping out there!"

"Oh, are they? Then perhaps you can tell us if it is a shark who is stealing our bait?"

"No," answered Raven slyly. "I don't think it's a shark. But it may well be the Gonaqadet who is tricking you."

"The Gonaqadet?" A look of fear came into the eyes of the men.

"Perhaps you'd better use bigger hooks—or different bait —and maybe try for halibut instead."

The men consulted together for a while, and then they began to cut up chunks of fat and place them on the halibut hooks. They paddled their canoes back into the bay again. Raven pulled his raven beak down, assumed his bird form, and flew after them. He could hardly wait to gobble up those luscious chunks of fat. He dived into the water, became a fish, and snatched from this hook and that. Each time the fishermen baited their lines, Raven waited till they were not looking, dived down, and stole the bait. Sometimes in his haste he even pulled off the hooks and broke the lines. The fishermen were so enraged they decided to continue fishing even if it should take the whole night to catch a single fish! They sat in their canoes, holding the lines in their hands and watching closely to see if they could spot the thief. But Raven was wily. He dived out of their sight and grabbed swiftly!

Finally, one of the fishermen pulled in his line very sharply just when Raven had grabbed the fat, and the hook stuck. He pulled and twisted violently. When the others saw the water thrashing, they came to help the fisherman. Raven called to the rocks on the sea bottom, "Rocks, hide me lest I perish!" But they would not. Then he saw some thick ropes of seaweed and cried, "Save me, Seaweed, my friend!" But the seaweed would not. Up, up the fishermen pulled the line, closer and closer. When he reached the surface, Raven was himself again. The hook was caught in his long black beak. He kicked against the underside of the canoe with his sharp claws. Suddenly he twisted his head. "Break then, old beak!" he exclaimed. "I'll get another one! No humble fisherman is going to catch Raven-Who-Sets-Things-Right like this!" With a wrench, Raven jerked his head to the side. He felt his beak crunch and snap—and suddenly he was free! Into the air he sprang, croaking hoarsely, leaving half his beak on the halibut hook. Once on land again, he pulled his mask up, changed to human form, and with his blanket covering his face, he waited for the fishermen. They had no trouble hauling in their lines now, and they did not guess that it had been Raven who had ruined their fishing. Hanging off one of the halibut hooks, when they landed, was a strange-looking object, pointed and dark with long, stringy seaweed entangled on its jagged edge. What could it be? They had never seen anything like it before. The fishermen passed it from one to another. Nobody knew!

Other villagers came down to the shore. They examined the object, turned it over, smelled it, and passed it around. "It surely belongs to a sea creature, some water monster. . . . The Gonaqadet?" they whispered, almost afraid to speak his name.

Raven, who had joined the crowd, waited anxiously for the object to be passed to him. Without his beak he couldn't eat, and that was terrible! At last it was his turn. He grasped the object and muttered, "Strange, strange, strange. It is an omen of evil! Something very bad will surely happen because of this!" He turned as he said it, about to clap the half beak back on his face, change to his bird shape, and fly away. But the half beak slipped from his grasp and fell to the sand. Before he could retrieve it, a greedy gull snatched it up and flew away with it.

"*Aaaaaaiiiii.* . . . Catch him . . . catch him . . . he has stolen the evil thing! We must get it back!" shouted Raven. It was too late; the gull had disappeared, and with it half of Raven's beak!

"It must indeed be the nose of the Gonaqadet!" muttered the villagers. "Woe to us if he comes here looking for it." They ran terrified back to the village, and Raven wandered morosely into the cedar forest. There he gathered a lump of spruce gum, shaped it and colored it to match the other half of his beak, and pressed it on. Then he departed in search of the gull.

The gull, meanwhile, had flown to another village. It had dropped the object, and some fishermen had found it and taken it to the chief's house. The chief examined it but at first could not make much of it. Then the Gonaqadet flashed through his mind! "It is the nose of the Gonaqadet, certainly! If we do not honor it, and he comes to look for it here, he will devour us all!" And saying this, the chief dipped the object respectfully in eagle down and, with great ceremony, hung it on the back post of his lodge.

Raven flew to all the houses in Kundji and looked down each smoke hole, but nowhere did he see his beak. So he flew on to the next village. Again he searched but found no sign of it. He heard whispers here and there: "The Gonaqadet has lost his nose! Have you heard? He may come ashore seeking it! Beware!"

Finally, Raven called to Eagle. "Eagle, my friend, come with me. Help me find my beak, or I will starve. I cannot go any place where men will see my broken beak, and I cannot catch food without it. Help me, my friend! I will wait at the smoke hole of the chief's lodge, in this next village. Go in, and ask if they have seen the nose of the Gonaqadet. Say that it is a sacred object with great spirit power, and you would like to see it. Say that your chief would like to touch it and learn about its great power. And ask for food—any kind of food! I'll wait above at the smoke hole. I am starving!"

Eagle joined Raven, and they flew to the next village. Raven waited while Eagle flew down and inquired about the nose of the Gonaqadet "for his chief." Nobody had seen it, but politely they offered him a bit of salmon to take to his chief.

"Oh, he never eats that!" said Eagle firmly, and he gulped down the salmon himself.

"A few salmonberries, then, for your chief?"

"Alas, my chief has a sickness in his belly, and he cannot eat them!" replied Eagle, and his eyes glittered as he gobbled up the berries.

"Surely you would like some ripe cranberries for him?"

Eagle shook his head sadly. "He is able to eat very little

at the moment!" replied Eagle, and he gulped noisily to drown the sound of Raven's hungry croaking. Then he returned to Raven.

"Why did you say those things when you know I'm dying of hunger?" demanded Raven. Eagle flapped his wings and flew away, laughing!

Raven traveled to the next village in his human form, holding his blanket across his face. Again he went from house to house, asking, "Have you seen an object, sharp and black, with seaweed fringing its edges?"

At last some of the people cried out, "An object, sharp and black, with seaweed hanging from its edges? It is the nose of the Gonaqadet, and it hangs in ceremony on the house post, in the lodge of our chief." So Raven went to the chief's house, and there he saw his beak, covered with eagle down, hanging on the post.

The chief said to him, "You are a stranger here. Enter, and be welcome."

"Yes," answered Raven. "I come from a village far from here. I come because I have heard that you have in your lodge a magic object of great power. I have come a long way to ask if I may just see this strange and wonderful thing."

"Ahhhh," replied the chief. "You may see it. Perhaps you will tell us what it is. We think it is the nose of the Gonaqadet!" He took it from the wall and passed it to Raven, whose hand trembled as he clutched it, so eager was he to get it back! But he pretended to look at it very closely.

"I cannot examine it well in this light . . . ," he murmured. "Perhaps you would be good enough to open the smoke hole a little wider so that I can see better?"

The chief ordered his servants to open up the smoke hole,

while Raven held the object close to his eyes. "Curious! Most strange! Surely it *is* the nose of the Gonaqadet!" he muttered. Suddenly he clapped it in place, over the sticky surface of his makeshift beak. At once he changed into his raven form and rose swiftly out through the smoke hole!

To this day there is an odd ridge on the raven's beak, as though it had been broken off and mended in a hurry!

—RETOLD BY DOROTHY DE WIT

Halibut Man and the House on the Waves

(PACIFIC COAST)

IN THE FIRST DAYS, IN A VILLAGE AT THE HEAD OF THE NASS River, the people were starving. Raven was hungry, too, for no fish swam in the rivers, and the fish in the sea stayed so far from shore that the fishermen could not catch them. It was said that far out in the ocean there floated a huge house, the Abundant House, in which all the herring, the salmon, and the halibut were kept captive. But where it was, and how to find it, no one knew. Raven resolved to find the house, and one morning he set forth early and flew far to the west.

Hour after hour he flew, and finally, he saw far below

him something that looked like a large animal. Gulls circled around it, screaming into the wind. Down Raven dived, and he saw that the something was a huge cedar house, with a wide doorway. He settled silently on the roof and looked down the smoke hole. Below was a very big room, and sitting on the floor was a strange, thin man with a long head and silvery scales covering his body.

The man lifted a board in the floor, let down a line, and pulled up a large halibut. Then Raven knew that this was, indeed, the Abundant House, where lived Halibut Man, the keeper of all the herring, the salmon, and the halibut of the seas. Raven's mouth watered, and he began to devise a plan to take over the Abundant House.

First, he flew swiftly back to the village and called all the fishermen together. He told them to carve a harpoon, with a very long line. The fishermen made the harpoon, and for the line they tried the sinews of first one animal and then another. But each time they tested the line it broke. At last, the tomtit, a tiny gray wren, offered to lend them his sinews, which were known to be exceedingly tough.

Raven showed the women how to braid a line from the tomtit's sinews, as thin as a spider web, long and very strong. Then the men fastened the harpoon firmly to a large, sturdy canoe and waited. Raven's plan was to fly to the Abundant House and lure Halibut Man away. Then he would fly back toward the village, and when he came in sight of the canoe, he would wheel and rise straight up in the air. At this signal, the men were to follow his flight.

Across the water to the house on the waves raced Raven. Halibut Man was sitting on the floor of his house, looking out to sea when Raven appeared. Halibut Man looked surprised when the bird flew in the door, and he was even more surprised when Raven said, "At last, at last, I have found you, my brother! Our poor father told me to look everywhere, till I found you!"

"Who are you?" asked Halibut Man suspiciously.

"I am Raven-Who-Sets-Things-Right. Everyone knows me!"

"I do not know you, and I have never even heard your name!" retorted Halibut Man rudely.

"Then you are the first not to have heard of me!" replied Raven. "I brought the Box of Daylight from the Over-Sky Country to the people. I stole fire and gave it to them. I found fresh water for them to drink. And I forced Tchanegoa, the Tide Woman, to hold back the waters of the sea once each day, so that the people could gather mussels, and crabs, and clams for food."

But Halibut Man still looked at Raven coldly. "I have been a man and lived in this house since the beginning of the world. I have no father, no mother, no family, for I was created when the world was made. I am Halibut Man!"

"Ahhhhh, there you are wrong, my brother!" Raven spoke very earnestly. "Our father from the Over-Sky Country lost you when you fell from there to the bottom of the sea! He has sent me in search of you, and I have flown everywhere, for he wishes to see his dear son again, after so long a time. Come with me, and I will take you to him. But first, I am very weary from flying, and I am terribly hungry!"

"Indeed, you must be hungry!" said Halibut Man. "I will feed you." He opened the floorboard and let down his line. After a few minutes he hauled it in, and a large halibut flapped at its end. He cut up the halibut and put it to steam.

While it was cooking, he turned to Raven, who had been examining the house and the smoke hole very carefully.

"You've made me wonder about my father. I would like to see if what you say is true. But I cannot fly, and I have no way of going to him."

Raven answered craftily, "Oh, that is no problem! I can carry you on my back. My wings are broad and very strong."

"Yes, but I am of the sea and have never traveled through the air. Suppose I should fall off! I might be killed!" Halibut Man shuddered at the thought but looked somewhat relieved at Raven's reply.

"Oh, you needn't worry. Your house is very large. Before we leave, I'll take you on my back and fly around in here so that you can practice holding on. It is very safe. You will like flying!"

Halibut Man climbed onto Raven's back, though somewhat fearfully. Raven flew about slowly and stayed close to the floor at first. But when he felt that Halibut Man sat securely on him, he mounted up to the smoke hole and flew out to sea.

"Sit firmly, Halibut Man," he called. "I am going to fly higher, toward the land where our father awaits you." And he flew farther and farther away from the Abundant House.

Then suddenly he flipped over and flew upside down! Down, down, down plunged Halibut Man into the cold waves. Raven righted himself and laughed! Now he could fly back to the villagers and the waiting fishermen.

But first, he would go back and gobble up the delicious halibut that was steaming in the house on the waves. When Raven had eaten the halibut, he was hungry for another.

He decided to catch one through the hole in the floor in the same way as Halibut Man had done. So he let down the line and croaked loudly in anticipation when he felt a bite.

But his croak stopped in midair as he drew up the line. Clutching it with both hands was Halibut Man! His fish eyes glared as he grabbed Raven's neck and twisted it.

"That will silence your lying tongue for good. Did you really think you could get rid of me by dropping me into the water when I can live in the sea anywhere as well as in my own house?"

Raven drifted on the waves, still, and apparently lifeless. The tide carried him landward and finally washed him ashore near his own village.

But Raven, though hurting all over, was by no means dead! As soon as he felt the sand under him, he lay there to rest for a while, then shook himself and spoke to the fishermen. "I will fly on a straight course to the Abundant House of Halibut Man. Follow me with the harpoon, and when you see me fly down to the roof, aim it at the house. Then—all of you—begin to sing. Sing loudly, and pull, pull, with all your might!"

Raven flew, straight as a dart, to the Abundant House, and when he landed, the fishermen threw the harpoon, with its tomtit line. The great hook buried itself in the wood of the house, and the wind snatched up the line and wrapped it around the building. Raven, on the roof, flapped his wings. The line grew taut as it began to pull the great structure toward the shore, slowly at first, then faster and faster, as it was caught by the current.

The singing of the fishermen grew louder and louder as

they neared the shore. Suddenly the door flew open, and Halibut Man leaped into the sea, where he swam deep below to the Kingdom Under the Waves.

And after him spilled forth a flood of herring, and salmon, and halibut, and oolachen!

"From now on," croaked Raven to the villagers, "all the fish of the sea are yours, and you need hunger no longer!"

The people sang and sang, till the songs filled the air, and the fish surged through the sea and up the rivers, for all the days to come.

And even now the villagers sing these same songs when it is the fishing season along the Nass River.

—RETOLD BY DOROTHY DE WIT

Far North
and Eskimo

The vast area stretching east from Greenland to the northeast corner of Siberia, as well as across the far north of the North American continent, was inhabited by a people who called themselves *Inuit*, the people. We call them Eskimos. Never far from some sea or coastal water, they lived in small villages or settlements, and in spite of different national backgrounds, because of the arctic environment of frozen seas, land, and tundra, they developed many traits in common. Life was short, many met death through fishing and hunting accidents, children were orphaned and families split up, and the quest for food was never-ending.

Thus, many of their stories were about the animals that lived with them or provided them with food. Others were about their environment—the "spirit-ball-players," whose game of tossing a walrus head back and forth across the heavens created the Northern Lights. Still others told of Sedna, the Mother of Seals. During the long nights, the

Eskimo people played cat's cradle with stretched sinews. There were endless variations. Or they carved animals from ivory, whalebone, abalone, or soapstone. And in the snow lodgings the grandmother or one of the elders of the family would narrate stories in the exact wording heard from the old ones.

Sometimes the family went to the Singing House, a large structure made of snow blocks, with seal-oil lamps fastened to a central pole. The guests placed themselves in a circle around the storyteller, who sat near the central pillar. The first stories were about historical events; then followed legends and folktales; and finally, recent feats of personal experiences. The guests responded to the teller when he beat a single-headed drum and sometimes danced his tale, with calls and chants.

On rare occasions the Angakok, who was shaman-conjuror-talebearer, might contact the spirit powers, aided by his Tornak (a helpful spirit).

The-Boy-Who-Snared-
the-Wind and the
Shaman's Daughter

(THOMPSON RIVER)

IN THE DAYS OF OUR GRANDFATHERS THE NORTH WIND RACED
fiercely across the land, uprooting trees, striking the lodgings,
and tearing up the earth. The people cringed and hid when
they heard his roar, for many had been killed, and the
North Wind paid no heed to their cries.

There was a man who lived near Spences Bridge with his
three sons. They hated the North Wind for its cruelty, yet
they could not think of a way to stop it. Every barricade,
every trap that they set, he tore apart and strewed across
the land.

Nevertheless, the youngest son, Sna-naz, was determined
to catch the wind and punish it. "I will set a snare for it,"
said Sna-naz. "I will make a noose of tough rawhide and
place it in the tunnel where the wind blows through the
rocks."

So he made a strong noose—a large one—and set it at

night in the tunnel where the wind blew most strongly. All night he waited, hidden from sight, and he heard the wind as it wrestled with the noose. Suddenly the wind screamed. It had gotten free and blew more fiercely than ever. The noose had not been tight enough to hold it.

The next night Sna-naz drew the rawhide tighter to make the opening narrower, but the wind ripped it savagely and ran away, leaving the broken thongs on the rocks. Each night Sna-naz listened and waited; each night the wind would not be trapped. Still, Sna-naz would not give up, and he tightened the noose a little more each night and waited.

One morning, as the sun rose, Sna-naz looked at his noose and saw he had caught the North Wind! Up and down, back and forth, around and around the North Wind twisted, but the snare was too tight, the noose too strong, and the rock tunnel too narrow. Sna-naz took his great blanket and threw it over the wind. Then he tied the blanket at the corners, making a strong sack, which he dragged with difficulty into the village. "I have caught North Wind!" he cried. "North Wind is a prisoner in my blanket!"

But the people laughed and did not believe him. "No," they said. "You are only a boy! You could not be so strong or cunning!" So Sna-naz loosened the sack a bit, and North Wind howled so that his terrible breath nearly blew apart the lodge. The people were terrified. "Quickly! Tie it up again lest it escape!" they screamed. "We believe you now."

Sna-naz quickly reknotted the blanket. He kept North wind tied up for days and nights until, after a very long time, the wind promised never again to ravage the land. Then Sna-naz carried the sack with North Wind still tied in it to a distant, barren spot, where he released it. North Wind crawled out, ashamed and humiliated, and never again was he rude or violent to those who lived on Thompson River. The people shouted and praised Sna-naz when he returned. "You must have a new name!" they said. "From now on you will be known as Little Blanket, the-boy-who-snared-the-wind." And everyone honored him for his strong medicine power in conquering the North Wind.

So time passed, and one morning Little Blanket woke feeling that something new and wonderful was waiting for him. He had had a dream about a rich and powerful shaman, a mighty chief, who lived far to the south with his beautiful daughter. So vivid had been his dream that Little Blanket determined to seek out the shaman and marry his daughter. He built a canoe, stored provisions in his parfleche, and, with his arrows and a strong new bow, set forth. For many days he was on the river, and many nights he watched his campfire burn to coals when he stopped to rest; but at last he came to the border of the shaman's country. He was glad, but he was afraid as well, for everywhere he had heard of the shaman's great magic and powerful medicine. The-boy-who-snared-the-wind hid his canoe in a cove near the river. First he sought the lodge of a wisewoman who lived nearby. He had heard that the shaman set difficult trials for any young man who sought the hand of his daughter. Many had tried, and failed, for the girl was known for her virtue and her beauty.

The old seeress had heard Little Blanket had tamed the wind, and she approved of his modesty and skill. "The shaman is a hard magician," she said. "He has strong magic, and he will make it very difficult for you. He is very jealous of his daughter and does not want her to marry and leave him." Little Blanket laid an offering in her lodge. He knew he could not hope to succeed without her counsel. "You must have the help of many of your animal brothers, great and small," she told him. "The loqkena ducks, the buffalo, the mountain goat ram, the ants, the large conch shell, the ati-tia bird, and the antelope. Do not be too proud to ask help of even the most humble of them, for you will surely need the special gifts of each one."

The loqkena ducks, the shell, the ants, and the ati-tia bird he found close at hand near the river. But he roamed the plain for many days to find the buffalo and climbed the high rocks to reach the mountain goat. He nearly lost his strength running to catch the fleet antelope. After each animal had agreed to help, he brought them back to his canoe. But when they all got in, the canoe nearly sank with their weight! Nevertheless, together they managed to paddle down the river until they neared the village. Little Blanket hid the canoe and his animal friends in a secret cove and continued on foot.

The shaman's lodge was beautiful and very large. The shaman looked severely at Little Blanket when he appeared before him. "You ask for my daughter. But you must have heard how many others have asked and been refused! Only he who proves wise, strong, skillful, and powerful in magic may claim my daughter. The trials are hard—few men can do what I demand!"

But Little Blanket said, "If you will, give me the chance to prove myself."

"Then we will begin," said the shaman. He lifted a copper paddle lying beside him and threw it far out into the lake nearby. It sank out of sight at once. "By noon tomorrow you must bring that copper paddle to me."

Little Blanket returned to the canoe. "Oh, loqkena ducks, will you dive for the copper paddle and bring it to me?" That night the ducks flew to the lake, dived now here, now there, and at last found the copper paddle and brought it to Little Blanket. The shaman was surprised when, at noon the next day, Little Blanket returned the paddle to him.

But quickly the shaman pointed out a large boulder. "You are strong, I have heard. It will then mean nothing to you to split that boulder! Tomorrow you must do so!" And the shaman smiled as he motioned the boy away.

Little Blanket returned to the cove. "Strong Buffalo, my brother, do you fear to test your strength against so grim a boulder?"

"No," said the buffalo. "I have pitted my strength against stronger objects than that! Tonight I will shatter the rock for you." And the next morning the shaman saw that the boulder had been broken into a hundred pieces.

Still, the shaman was not satisfied. He pointed to a rocky crag rising high above a mass of sharp rocks. "You must leap from that crag and land below on your head," he said to Little Blanket.

Little Blanket saw that the shaman was trying to kill him. He went to the mountain goat. "My friend with the mighty horns, will you lend me your tremendous strength and sense of balance?" The ram went to the rock with Little Blanket, who sprang from the craggy precipice and landed on his head unharmed. The mountain goat had given him his powers.

Then the shaman ordered that many sacks filled with

tiny beads be carried to a grassy meadow and spilled every-where. "Truly you are strong and wise, Little Blanket!" said the shaman. "But are you also deft and clever with your hands and sharp of sight? For if you are not, you will never be able to find and string these beads, each color on a separate string, by tomorrow!" The shaman felt sure this was a task that could not be done, and he was pleased with himself.

But now, Little Blanket turned to the ants. "Oh, small ones who move so surely and quickly, will you help me?" At once a procession of tiny ants moved across the plain to the meadow. They were joined by others who lived nearby. Through the hours they worked, and by early morn-ing the beads lay in long threads of bright red, indigo, green, and yellow before the entrance of the shaman's lodge.

"Now may I have your daughter's hand?" asked Little Blanket.

But the shaman shook his head. "You are brave and cun-ning, and you are willing to work. But I am not sure your magic is as strong as it must be if you are to become my son-in-law. There is a chief who lives in another land far from here. He will send me a message. You must listen and by tomorrow repeat his every word."

Sadly Little Blanket returned to the cove. This was a difficult task indeed! As he sat and thought, his eye fell on the conch shell "Ah, my brother, with your large rosy ear, can you not hear the chief's message?" He placed the ear of the conch against the earth. Many hours Little Blanket sat beside it in silence and waited.

At last the conch said, "Pick me up, and listen carefully." And as Little Blanket put the conch to his ear, he heard clearly the distant chief's message. The shaman marveled when Little Blanket repeated each word to him.

But the next day he had still another test. "My daughter is as fleet of foot as a deer. She would not want a husband she could beat! Tomorrow you must race her and win, or you will lose her!"

Little Blanket went back to his animal friends. This time he spoke to the antelope. "Oh, fleet of foot beyond all others, lend me, I beg, the speed I need to race the shaman's daughter and win," he said.

Early the next day, when the two runners set forth together, the boy did not feel his footsteps any swifter than usual; but as they ran and ran, he felt his breath come more strongly, and his feet became winged, so that long before the girl reached the goal, he had arrived and was waiting for her. She was not sorry to take his hand and bring him to her father.

The shaman by now was satisfied that Little Blanket had strong magic, great wisdom, strength, and modesty, yet he demanded a last trial of him. "My son-in-law must be fleet of foot, and brave, and cunning, and that you have shown yourself to be. Yet one thing is needed. He must also love beauty and be able to make music for my daughter." Now Little Blanket knew exactly what to do. He cut a reed from the riverbank, shaped it into a flute, and whispered a message to the little ati-tia bird. The songbird lent his liquid notes to Little Blanket's flute as he walked to the shaman who stood waiting in front of the lodge with his daughter. Little Blanket played his longing and his love on the flute, and when the girl heard his music, she smiled and went forth to meet him.

Then Little Blanket knew that he had won, for the shaman decreed feasting and dancing to welcome his son-in-law, "whose magic," said the old chief, "is stronger than mine!" The people celebrated long, and then Little Blanket and his wife returned to the canoe for the journey to Little Blanket's home. They thanked their animal helpers, who also returned to their homes.

And the-boy-who-had-snared-the-wind and the shaman's daughter remembered them with gratitude for all the years of their lives.

—RETOLD BY DOROTHY DE WIT

The Angakok and the Mother of Seals

(ESKIMO)

THE SINGING HOUSE OF THE VILLAGE WAS CROWDED. ALL thirty people of the igloos were gathered in the big snow lodge, which they had built for their celebrations.

The older women sat at the back, close to the curved snow wall of the igloo. The younger women and their children made up the middle circle. And in the very front were the men.

But the men, too, had pushed themselves back so as to

leave an open space in the center for Old Mitek. He was their wise man, their Angakok. And all eyes were upon him.

"Tonight Mitek will go down under the sea to find Sedna, the Mother of Seals." This was the message that had gone the rounds of the snow houses of the village that day.

"It is good!" the people said to one another. "The Seal Mother is angry. We know that from the terrible blizzards she sends us. Only a visit from Mitek can make her happy once more. Only he can persuade her to still the North Wind and let her seals come again to their breathing holes in the ice."

The people of this tiny village lived far, far to the north on the shore of the Arctic Ocean. It was a time, long ago, when the people believed in spirits like Sedna, the Mother of Seals.

Mitek, with his white hair and wrinkled brown face, was old and wise. Everyone knew he could talk to the spirits. With his charms and chants, he could cure sickness. That is why he had become their medicine man or, as the people called him, their Angakok.

It was hot inside the Singing House. Heat rose from the soapstone lamps on the little shelves cut into the snow walls. More warmth came from so many people crowded together in the airless igloo. Most of the men and women had thrown off their furry caribouskin parkas. Even so, drops of perspiration stood out on their faces.

Mitek stood in the very center of the igloo, not far from the smoke hole in the rounded roof. His only garments were his short caribouskin trousers and his bearskin boots, and of course, he still wore his Angakok's seal-hide belt with its magic charms. The children, especially a bright-eyed boy named Papik, counted these charms to make sure all were there: the caribou tooth, the raven's claw, the tiny model of a kayak, and a bit of carved walrus ivory. Papik knew them by heart.

The journey which Old Mitek was about to make to the undersea of the Mother of Seals was important to all in the Singing House. By now the caribou meat from the summer hunting was almost gone. Great blizzards had kept the hunters from going out to the seals' breathing holes with their harpoons. Even on days when they dared brave the weather, they came home empty-handed.

Everyone was hungry. There was no doubt but that Sedna was angry. Why else would she keep her seals from coming to the breathing holes?

Now it was the dark of the moon. There was not even a faint glow in the sky. The time was right for Old Mitek to make his visit to Sedna, Mother of Seals.

"I'm ready now. Bind my arms and my legs!" The Angakok was squatting down in the center of the open space cleared for him. Two young Eskimo hunters stepped forward. With long strips of seal hide, they tied Mitek's arms and legs so that he could not possibly rise from the floor.

"Put out the lamps! All eyes must be closed!" The Angakok's voice was loud. Everyone obeyed his command. That is, everyone but Papik. He opened his narrow eyes for just one last look. But the room was so dark that he could see nothing. And before his eyes could become used to the darkness, he felt a hand slide gently across them. It was the hand of his mother, he knew. She would not risk her son's being hurt by the magic of the Angakok, who would be very angry if he saw that the boy was peeking.

In the Singing House not a sound was to be heard except the excited breathing of the people. Then Old Mitek, the Angakok, began to chant.

"*Ha-la-la! Ha-la-la!* My body grows light. Light as a little bird's feather, it is. Like a dry stick on the ocean, it floats, oh, it floats!"

The old man's voice seemed to come from under the ceiling of the Singing House, though Papik knew Old Mitek must still be sitting where he had been tied on the snow floor. But then, what was whirling and whizzing around the igloo? Surely it had to be the Angakok's spirit rising in the air.

"I fly like a bird up over your heads. Now I go out of the smoke hole. *Ha-la-la! Ha-la-la!*" The Angakok's voice was growing fainter. The people could hardly hear his last words. "My guardian spirit is leading the way to the home of the Seal Woman."

The whizzing noise was gone. For a few moments there was only silence in the darkness of the Singing House. Then to make the waiting easier, someone began to sing, softly. It was a song about Sedna which everyone knew, and all joined in.

The song told the sad story of the Mother of Seals. She had once been a human girl who had refused to marry the old man her father had chosen for her husband! She had, instead, become the bride of the handsome young hunter whom she loved.

In those times, it was said, animal creatures could take on the forms of human beings. And this young hunter, in truth, was the wild seabird known as a petrel.

It is not strange that Sedna's father should have been angry and gone after her. But he need not have been so cruel. He snatched her away from her beloved young husband and dragged her into his boat.

He had hardly paddled from the shore when black storm clouds hid the sky and winds arose that blew the waves up into mountains of dark water.

"Turn back to the shore, father!" Sedna begged. "My husband is angry. He will upset your boat. He is no ordinary man, but a sea petrel disguised in man's form. And he rides on the storm."

Her father tried with all his might to keep his boat right side up. But above him in the dark sky, among the racing clouds, he saw a giant petrel flapping its long wings.

"Unlucky girl!" he cried to Sedna, crouched at his feet. "Because of you, my boat will be lost, and I, too, will be lost; but your petrel will never have you!" And he threw the girl out of the canoe into the foaming waves.

Sedna caught hold of the canoe's edge. There she clung fast, lest she be drowned.

"Let go, girl, let go!" Her father tried to loosen her hold. And when she would not let go, he brought the sharp edge of the paddle down on her fingers, again and again. The sharp edge of the paddle cut off her fingers, and they sank down, down into the ocean. But as they sank, each little finger joint turned into a seal.

Sedna herself floated safely to the sea bottom, and it was there she lived still, so the song said. And from her open-roofed igloo she ruled the seals, descendants of those that had been created from her fingers.

As the song ended, Old Mitek's voice was heard again. It sounded as if it came from far, far away. "I am floating in through the smoke hole." The voice was growing louder. "I have returned from the sea. Light the lamps now."

In the smoky light of the seal-oil lamps, Papik could see that the old man's arms and legs were still tied with the hide straps. And it did not seem odd to him that no drop of seawater hung to his body or clothes. Papik understood that it was only the Angakok's spirit that had gone down under the waves.

The Angakok stood up and stretched his arms high over his head. "I found Sedna in her igloo. I broke down the guard wall around it. I did not let her fierce dog stop me from going inside. There Sedna sat, with her seals crowded around her. Her back was toward me, and I could see her long hair, dirty and tangled, hanging over her shoulders. She was in a sad state, and angry, too. Her face was as dark as the storm clouds."

Every woman and girl in the Singing House cried softly. They were sorry for Sedna, who, without any fingers, could not get the shells and the sand and the tangles out of her hair. Then the Angakok told how he had turned the Seal Woman around to face him, and how he had gently taken the seaweed out of her hair with his own fingers, and how he had smoothed it. Then Sedna smiled and had made him a feast of seal liver.

"One by one, Sedna pushed the seals out of her igloo." And Mitek's voice was triumphant. "Tomorrow there will be seals at the breathing holes. Tomorrow we will have good hunting weather. For when Sedna smiles, no blizzard will come."

Papik wondered how the Angakok could have traveled so far and done so much in such a short time. Then he remembered that the old man had told him that time under the sea was not at all like time on the land. A few minutes on earth could be many hours on the floor of the ocean.

And no one could deny that the next day's weather was good or that the seals had again come to the breathing holes in the frozen ocean.

—FROM WONDER TALES OF SEA AND SHIPS
BY FRANCES CARPENTER

The Day Tuk
Became a Hunter

(ESKIMO)

THERE WAS ONCE A BOY NAMED TUK. HE DREAMED OF BE-coming a great hunter like his father. He pictured himself hunting seals and deer, walruses and wolves. Sometimes, when he felt especially brave, he even imagined himself hunting polar bears.

During the long winter nights Tuk helped his father, Isupik, sharpen his spears and knives and prepare the dog sled for the next day's hunt. Tuk worked hard. He learned eagerly everything his father would teach him.

When work was done, Tuk often took out his own ax and knife, and he carved toys out of stone for his sister and himself. Tuk made wonderful dolls that his sister could dress up in sealskin clothes. But he carved fierce animals for himself. And while he carved, he dreamed of the day when he would be a brave and skillful hunter.

One day Isupik let Tuk join him on a hunting trip. Tuk smiled proudly as their dogs pulled the sled across the frozen land. They were not far from home when Isupik touched Tuk on the shoulder and pointed straight ahead. They halted the dogs, and Tuk saw a large, fat seal lying on the ice. Isupik slipped down onto his hands and knees and crawled toward the seal with his spear in his hand.

But as he moved ahead, a huge white polar bear, hiding behind banks of snow, crept silently toward him. When the bear was close enough to attack, he sprang at Isupik and knocked his spear out of his hand. Isupik reached for his knife, but the bear threw him down and pinned him against the ice.

Tuk pulled out his ax, ran to Isupik, and started to swing at the bear. "Run, Tuk!" Isupik cried. But Tuk struck the bear again and again. The bear held Isupik with one paw and swung at Tuk with the other. Then, grunting with fury, he let go of Isupik and went after Tuk.

Isupik leaped up and ran for the sled. He raced the dogs toward Tuk, who hopped on the sled, and they rode swiftly home. When the dogs saw the igloo, they turned sharply toward it, and Isupik's spears and knives rolled off the sled.

When Tuk and Isupik arrived at the igloo, they quickly unharnessed the dogs, ran through the igloo tunnel, and sealed the entrance with a block of snow. Safely inside, they looked through the clear ice window and saw the bear. He had followed them home. Isupik glanced around and realized he had no weapons. He had lost them all during the race home.

Day after day Isupik and Tuk watched the white bear through the ice window. He paced angrily back and forth, pawing at the igloo, circling it again and again. Each day the family awoke hoping that the huge bear would be gone, but he was always there.

After many days, there was no food left. Now they had to choose: either to starve in the igloo or to fight the bear with the hope of killing him. "Wait, Father," said Tuk. "Let us wait a little longer. Perhaps he will go away." But the bear stayed.

One night Tuk was awakened by the light of the full moon that streamed into the igloo. He jumped out of the fur blankets, dressed, and peered out the ice window. As he looked across the fields of snow, he saw the bear sleeping in the moonlight, and a plan began to form in his mind. He found his small carving knife and quietly sharpened it on a stone.

Then Tuk crept into the igloo tunnel and gently removed the snow block from the entrance. The ice and snow sparkled in the light of the full moon. Tuk crawled out of the tunnel and quietly began to build a huge snowbank beside it. Once, while he was working, the bear snorted and turned, and Tuk jumped into the tunnel. But he came out again when the bear was quiet, and with his knife he began to carve the snowbank.

Toward morning, as the sky brightened, Tuk finished his

work. He stood back and looked at his sculpture. He had carved a vicious-looking bear even larger and more frightening than the polar bear. Then he silently crawled back into the igloo to wait for the bear to awaken.

Tuk watched the sleeping bear through the ice window. The sun was beginning to come over the horizon. The bear moved and yawned. He stretched and looked around. Suddenly he caught sight of the huge snow bear glistening in the sun, and he jumped up. He froze in his tracks, unable to move, as he stared at the snow bear in terror.

At that moment Tuk rushed to the tunnel. He crawled through it on his hands and knees, aware that any sudden movement or noise might awaken the bear out of his terrified trance. With his knife lifted high, Tuk came out of the tunnel and, springing swiftly toward the bear, plunged it into the animal's chest and drew it out again. The bear buckled for a moment and then swung his paws at Tuk. But Tuk drove the knife in again. The bear fell, and with a great gasp he rolled over and died.

Isupik ran out of the igloo and watched with pride as Tuk began to carve up the bear. He was a great hunter now, for he had killed their enemy and had provided food for his family.

—FROM THE DAY TUK BECAME A HUNTER AND OTHER STORIES
   BY RONALD MELZACK

Canada

The Native Americans of Canada are spread from the western forests and prairies to the Mackenzie River, the Caribou country of central Canada, eastward to the Maritime Provinces. The Athapaskan people were influenced by the tribes of the Columbia River basin and the plateau in the United States. Cree and Chipewyan tribes reached to the Arctic and the tundra; and the Abenaki and the Micmac, who called themselves Children of the Dawn Country, people of the East, lived north of the Woodland tribes of New England.

For the Caribou Indians, the great animal for which they were named meant food, shelter, and clothing. Snowshoes, furs, toboggans were essential in the bitter winters, and hunger was a driving force. Though they were an inland and river people, some of their legends and myths remind us of those of the Pacific seafarers.

Among the Micmac and other eastern tribes, Glooscap was the culture hero. It was believed he lived on Blomidon, overlooking the Atlantic waters, and, by shooting special arrows into an ash tree, had brought forth the "children of light." He also created water for drinking, food and the knowledge of how to cultivate it, and many other good things for man's welfare. Glooscap (Gluskabe, Kulaskap, Gloskap) wandered everywhere, leaving his huge footprints on the eastern landscape and creating lakes, rocks, mountains as he walked the earth. At times he was accompanied by Marten, or Rabbit, or Badger.

Unlike any other shape-changer–trickster figure, Glooscap was kindly, wise, teasing, but beneficent and generous. He sailed westward in his great canoe after he had tamed the elements, but one day he would return, the Micmac believed.

The Boy Who
Was Called Thickhead

(ABENAKI)

THREE BROTHERS LIVED WITH THEIR OLD MOTHER IN A FOREST
near the sea. Their father had long been dead. At his death
he had owned little, and so his widow and her sons were
left very poor. Game was not plentiful where they lived,
and to get food enough to keep them from want, they often
had to go far into the forest. The youngest boy was smaller
and weaker than the others, and when the two older sons
went far away to hunt, they would never allow him to go
with them. He had to do all the work about the house, and
all day long he gathered wood in the forest and carried water
from the stream. And even when his brothers went out in
the springtime to draw sap from the maple trees, he was not
permitted to go with them. He was always making mistakes
and doing foolish things. His brothers called him Thickhead, and the people round about said he was a simpleton
because of his slow and queer ways. Only his mother was
kind to him, and she always said, "They may laugh at you

and call you fool, but you will prove to be the wisest of them all."

The chief of this tribe had a beautiful daughter who had many suitors. But her father turned them all away and said, "My daughter is too young to marry, and when the time comes, she will marry only a man who can make great profit from hunting." The older two sons decided that one of them must win the girl. It was now autumn, and the hunter's moon had come. They prepared to set out on a great hunting expedition far away in the northern forest. The youngest wanted to go with them. He had never been away from home, and he wished to see the world, and his mother said he might go. His brothers were very angry. "Much good Thickhead can do us in the chase," they said. "He will bring us only bad luck. He is a scullion and a drudge fit only for the fireside." But this time their mother commanded them to take him along, and they had to obey. So the three brothers set out for the north country.

The hunting was good, and the two older brothers killed many animals—deer and rabbits and otters and beaver. They came home bearing a great quantity of dried meat and skins, and each of them thought: "We have begun to prove our prowess, and if we succeed as well next year when the hunter's moon comes again, one of us will surely win the chief's daughter when she is old enough to marry."

All the youngest boy brought home was a large earthworm as thick as his finger and as long as his arm. It was the biggest earthworm he had ever seen. He had thought it such a curiosity and had been so busy watching it that he had had no time to hunt. His brothers said to their mother, "What did we tell you about Thickhead? Now he has surely proved himself a fool. He has caught only a fat earthworm in all these weeks." And they spread the story about in the village. Everybody laughed at the simpleton, and "Thickhead's Hunt" became a byword among them.

But the boy's mother only smiled and said, "He will surprise you all yet."

The boy kept the earthworm in a tiny pen, just outside the door of his home. One day a large duck came waddling along, and sticking her bill over the little fence of the pen, she quickly gobbled up the worm. The boy was very angry, and he went to the man who owned the duck and said, "Your duck ate my worm. I want my worm." When the man offered to pay him whatever price he asked, the boy said, "I do not want your money. I want my pet worm."

But the man said, "How can I give you your worm when my duck has eaten it up? It is gone forever."

And the boy said, "It is not gone; it is in the duck's belly, so I must have the duck."

Finally, the man gave Thickhead the duck, for he thought to himself, "What is the use of arguing with a fool?"

The boy took the duck home and made a pen for it. He tied a weight to its foot so that it could not fly away. He was quite happy again, for he thought, "Now I have both my worm and the duck." But one day a fox came prowling along looking for food. He saw the fat duck tied by the foot in the pen, and in a twinkling he was over the fence. The duck quacked and made a great noise, but she was soon silenced. The fox had just finished eating up the duck when the boy, who had heard the quacking, came running out of the house. The fox was smacking his lips after his good meal, and he was too slow in getting away. The boy beat him with a stout club and soon killed him. He threw the body into the yard behind the house. And he thought, "That is not so bad. Now I have my worm, and the duck, and the fox."

That night an old wolf came through the forest. He was very hungry, and in the bright moonlight he saw the dead fox lying in the yard. He pounced upon it greedily and devoured it until not a trace of it was left. But the boy saw him. And before the wolf could get away, he stole up on him and killed him with a blow of his ax. "I am surely in good luck," he thought, "for now I have the worm and the duck and the fox and the wolf."

But the next day, when he told his brothers of his good fortune and his great skill, they laughed loudly and said, "Much good a dead wolf will do you. Before two days have passed, it will be nothing but an evil-smelling thing, and we will have to bury it. You are indeed a great fool."

The boy thought over what they had said. "Perhaps they are right," he decided. "The dead wolf cannot last long. I will save the skin."

So he skinned the wolf and dried the skin and made a drum from it. The boy beat the drum each evening and made a great noise, and he was very proud because he had the only drum in the village. One day the chief sent for him and said, "I want to borrow your drum for this evening. I am giving a party to announce that my daughter is now old enough to marry. We have no musical instruments, and I want your drum, and I myself will beat it for the dancing."

So Thickhead brought his drum to the chief's house. But he was unhappy because he had not been invited to the feast while his brothers were among the favored guests, and he said to the chief, "Be very careful. Do not tear the skin of my drum, for I can never get another like it. My worm and my duck and my fox and my wolf all have helped make it."

The next day he went to get his drum back, but the chief had struck it too hard and had split it open. It was ruined beyond repair. The chief offered to pay Thickhead a great price for it, but the boy said, "I do not want your money. I want my drum. Give me back my drum for my worm, and my duck, and my fox, and my wolf are all in it."

The chief said, "I cannot give back your drum because it is beyond repair. But I will give you anything you desire in exchange for it. Name your price, and I will pay it."

And Thickhead thought to himself, "Here is my chance for good fortune."

"Since you cannot give me my drum," he said, "I will take your daughter in marriage instead."

The chief was upset, but he had given his word. Thickhead and the girl were married. She brought him much treasure, and they lived very happily together. His brothers were angry because they had failed, but their mother said, "I told you he would outwit you all, though you called him thickhead and fool, for the forest fairy told me so when he was born."

—From Canadian Wonder Tales by Cyrus Macmillan

Why Bootup, the Whale, Smokes a Pipe

(MICMAC)

ON THE ISLAND OF BLOMIDON, GLOOSCAP, THE MASTER, dwelled, surrounded by many animal and bird friends. Old Dame Bear kept his great wigwam in order and cared for Marten, Little Brother. Two tiny dogs guarded the great one, and though they were not much bigger than large mice, they barked loudly and were quick to give warning of danger.

Glooscap had done much to make life good for the people, for he was their friend and teacher. He had given names to the stars and constellations. And he had shown them how to hunt, how to cure skins, how to fish, and how to turn soil to bring forth a harvest. All the people knew that was good and wise, Glooscap had taught them.

One time Glooscap had gone on a trip for some weeks to see how things were working out. While he was away, Win-pe, the wicked wizard, had stealthily paddled his canoe to Blomidon. He had muzzled the dogs and stolen them, Dame Bear, and Marten. He was paddling away when Glooscap appeared. Though Glooscap was too late to reach the canoe, he shouted to Dame Bear somehow to get the little dogs back to shore. Dame Bear found a wooden dice platter that Win-pe had stowed in the canoe and placed the small creatures on it. Then she set the platter afloat toward Glooscap, who waded out and rescued the dogs.

Meanwhile, Win-pe paddled furiously southward, and the canoe and its captives disappeared from sight.

Seven years Glooscap waited. By then he believed Win-pe would have exhausted his sorcerer's bag of tricks and would no longer be able to hide Dame Bear and Little Brother. And so Glooscap set out with his little dogs to find Grandmother Bear and Marten.

The enormous canoe in which Glooscap had first come to the island was too cumbersome, so he stood on the shore and, softly at first, then more loudly, began to sing the song which called the whales from the deep. A young whale heard his call and at once swam toward Blomidon. When it lifted its head and saw Glooscap, it floated near the shore. But no sooner had Glooscap put his huge foot on its back than the whale sank below the water, Glooscap's weight was so great. So Glooscap thanked the whale and told it to return home.

Again he sang the whale call, even more loudly this time. And the greatest of all the whales in the sea heard and swam to him. And this time, when Glooscap set his foot on her mighty back, so large was the whale that she hardly felt him. Glooscap picked up his little guardians and, seated on her strong back, directed the whale to sail far out and south toward what is now Newfoundland. At first she swam slowly, for she was afraid of becoming shoaled on a sandbar. But when Glooscap urged her on, she swam strongly and made great speed.

At last the cliffs of a distant land rose on the horizon, and the whale swam toward the shoreline. After a while, however, as she looked down into the water, the whale saw large seashells. "I see shells below. Is that shape just ahead that looks like a giant bowstring not land?" the whale asked fearfully.

But Glooscap deceived her, for he wanted to come nearer to shore. "We are still a great way off," he said. "Swim on, Bootup, my friend." And the whale swam on.

Soon, however, the whale again felt that the water was becoming shallower and cried out, "Glooscap, my master! I hear the clams under the sands! They are singing to me, and I am afraid! What are they saying, Glooscap? I do not understand the words of the Clam People!"

Glooscap understood the words very well, for he knew all languages. He heard the clams' words of warning: "Ah, whale, take care! The Mighty Glooscap is leading you to the shoals! Throw him off your back, and swim out to sea! Quickly, before it is too late!"

The Clam People did not like Glooscap at all, and they would gladly have seen him drown!

But Glooscap said, "They are chanting a sea song":

> Hurry! Hurry! Hurry!
> Glooscap rides the sea,
> The great one rides
> To rescue old Dame Bear
> To rescue Little Brother!
> Hurry, hurry over the water!
> Faster, faster, go faster!

And Glooscap smiled as Bootup beat her strong fins

against the waves and pushed toward shore with tremendous speed.

Suddenly, the whale felt the rocks, then the sand of a bank, and the sharp shells on the shoal digging into her! "Alas, Glooscap! I am lost, for I am caught on a shoal! You have deceived me, my grandson, and now I must die."

But Glooscap leaped from the whale's broad back and, standing on the shore with his dogs, called gratefully, "You will not die, Bootup! Have no fear. I, Glooscap, send you back to your ocean depths." And with that he pressed his great bow against the whale's head and pushed her out toward the deep water.

Bootup rejoiced, but before the whale had swum very far, she called, "Glooscap, have you not some small gift for my service to you?"

And Glooscap laughed, for he knew before the whale spoke what she wanted. "A small thing, my grandson! An old pipe, like the one you have, and a little tobacco. Surely you can give that to this old one, to delight her days?"

So Glooscap filled a small pipe and put it in the whale's great mouth and lighted it. As the whale swam away, she puffed strongly, and the smoke rose out of her blowhole in a white arch against the sky. Glooscap leaned on his great bow, and said, "Smoke your little pipe with joy, old one. Men will say, when they see that white plume above your head, 'Behold! Bootup, the whale, is smoking the pipe the Great Glooscap gave her!'"

And so it has been to this very day!

—RETOLD BY DOROTHY DE WIT

The Magic Snowshoes

(MICMAC)

IN A HURON CAMP, BESIDE THE RIVER HOCHELAGA, THERE
lived a Micmac boy and his mother taken prisoner a dozen
years before. The boy, whose name was Wokun, was a baby
when captured and could not even remember his homeland.

"Someday, when you are a grown man," said his mother,
"we will escape and return to the Micmac country." It
seemed to Wokun that growing up would take forever.
Meanwhile, he was the butt of all the jokes and games in
the Huron camp.

"Porcupine eater! Only a poor ignorant Micmac eats porcupine!" It was no good saying that porcupine meat was
very good, provided it was cooked properly. The important
thing was to bear all and make no outcry or complaint, or
they would think him a coward and make life even more
miserable.

Wokun's only happy times were with his mother alone in
the woods when they were sent to cut up the hunters' game.
There they could talk freely of the home he had never
seen and the great hero, Glooscap, who watched over his
Wabanaki and helped them when they were in trouble.

"Blomidon is a long way off." Wokun sighed. "Glooscap
has forgotten us."

"Not so," said his mother. "He will help us when we

really need him. We must first do all we can to show by our courage and industry that we deserve his help." So she showed Wokun how to practice blowing feathers and outrun them in order to grow swift-footed, how to pound fish bones to dust and blow them against the wind to make his lungs strong. She made him a map of the Wabanaki country and taught him the history and language of his own people. She even made him a miniature Micmac moccasin and pressed it into the ground so Wokun would recognize its shape if ever he saw it on the trail.

The boy looked around at the quiet forest and cried longingly, "Why can't we run away?"

"The enemy would soon catch us and bring us back," said his mother, "to worse trials and closer imprisonment. It is a long way to our own country, my son, and our people fear the Huron. We must be quiet so that they will not be suspicious until the right time comes."

Events, however, crowded down on Wokun that very day. Back in camp, the Huron chief caught the boy's mother in some fancied wrong and began to beat her. Wokun rushed to his mother's defense and in his wild fury knocked the chief down, adding insult to injury by cutting off his scalp lock while he lay unconscious.

"Now all is lost," his mother moaned as the Huron dragged her son to a post in the center of the camp and tied him there, promising he would be put to death on the following day. The boys threw stones at him, but Wokun did not cry out, not once, and at last they tired of the sport and went to their lodges to sleep.

When all was still, Wokun wept quietly in the darkness, not for his hurts or the thought of tomorrow, but because now he would never grow up to see his own country and take his mother back to it. He hardly heard the soft rush of air close by, or the rustle of feathers, until a giant gray heron settled on the ground and he heard it speak.

"Well done, Wokun!" The boy expected the whole camp to waken at the thunderous voice, yet no one even stirred. Then he guessed that he and only he could hear the voice.

"Glooscap?" he asked, trembling between hope and fear.

The heron nodded gravely. "You have honored me and your people with your courage."

"Oh, master, help us to get back to our own country."

"Breathe in three times," commanded the Lord of Men and Beasts, and Wokun obeyed. Once, twice, thrice, and with each breath he grew larger until at last his bonds snapped and he stood free.

"Thank you, master!" Then Glooscap told him to go to his mother and say he must leave without her.

"Your mother is too old to travel as you must travel. She will be safe, I promise you. Tell her you will return with help as soon as you find your own people. When I am gone, break that stick on the ground, and it will become a pair of snowshoes. With them you can travel over ice or snow, under the snow, and even over the treetops." And with a rush of his great wings, he was gone.

Wokun did all that Glooscap had told him. Then, putting on the magic showshoes, he set off at top speed. When dawn lighted the camp a short time later, the Huron saw their prisoner had escaped and started in furious pursuit, confident that they would catch him easily before he reached the river. If not, however, the river would surely stop him. At this time of year it was only partly frozen and full of ice floes. To cross, it was necessary to haul the canoes up on the ice every so often and carry them to the next stretch of open water, and this work called for two strong men.

But Wokun, with his magic snowshoes, needed no canoe! The astounded Huron saw him leap from shore and land squarely on the nearest ice floe, and even as they launched their canoes, Wokun was halfway across, leaping from floe to floe on his marvelous footgear. The Huron reached the other side with the utmost difficulty and, putting on their own snowshoes, set off again in pursuit. When they were almost upon him, to their fresh astonishment Wokun dived under the snow, snowshoes and all!

"Now we have him!" They shouted after they got over their surprise. And they thrust their spears in the snow here, there, and everywhere, but no matter where they thrust or poked, Wokun wasn't there!

He traveled along under the snow for some distance before coming up for a breath of air. Looking back, he saw the Huron waving their spears at him and laughed. He gave them a mocking wave and sprang to a branch of the nearest tree. From there he leaped to another. This was too much for the Huron! Seeing a man on snowshoes leap from tree to tree like a squirrel, they lost heart and gave up the chase. They knew magic when they saw it, and who could fight magic? They hurried back to camp to tell their tale and to cast respectful side glances at the mother of the "magician"—which assured her she was now safe from harm.

Wokun traveled through the treetops until he thought himself beyond the reach of the enemy, then dropped to the snowy ground and traveled in the usual way. Now the land appeared softly green and pleasant with hills and valleys, beautiful as his mother had said. On the soft ground he saw a footprint and studied it. It was the mark of a moccasin, the exact shape of the one made by his mother. He was certainly in Micmac territory at last.

"Down with the Huron!" A great shout, then a chorus of angry yells shattered the silence, and he thought for a moment the enemy had caught him.

"Kill him, kill him!" The words were in his mother's tongue. These were Micmac!

"I am a Micmac like yourselves," he cried, and seeing them pause, he pulled something from his belt and cast it on the ground. "Look! The scalp lock of a Huron chief!" At that sure proof, the Micmacs put away their knives, asking his name and where he came from. Wokun told his story and begged them to return with him to save his mother.

At this they shook their heads and frowned. "They are too many for us!"

"Not if we can surprise them," pleaded Wokun. They agreed to consider the matter in council, and each brave spoke his views in turn. At the end Wokun spoke again.

"They are men like ourselves, no stronger and no braver. We can give them such a battle they will never trouble us again. Remember the wrongs they have done us, the women and children taken captive, the young braves slain. Remember how Glooscap helped me in my need and now he will help again if we need him."

Then one young brave sprang up and began to stamp his feet in approval. Soon all the rest joined in. The war dance was performed, and they set out for the country of the Huron with Wokun as guide.

Winter had settled in around the Huron country. Rivers

and lakes were hard under a blanket of snow, but this was good, for on snowshoes they could move quickly. When they reached the great river, they found it solidly frozen and crossed at night without difficulty. So rapidly and silently did they approach the Huron were taken completely by surprise. Wokun and the Micmac were able to storm the palisades and overwhelm the enemy within. When the Huron saw Wokun of the supernatural snowshoes, their courage was shaken, and they gave up after a short struggle.

So Wokun's mother was carried back in triumph to her own land, and the Micmac marveled at the great power and goodness of Glooscap, who watched over his people and helped them, even when they were far from home.

And now—*kespeadooksit!*—the story ends!

—From More Glooscap Stories by Kay Hill

Badger and the Green Giant

(MICMAC)

THERE WAS IN THE OLD TIME A GREAT ROGUE NAMED BADGER. The Wabanaki storytellers, who talked of men as though they were animals and animals as though they were men, spoke of Badger sometimes as a man and sometimes as an animal. But whether as man or animal, it was agreed that he had something of Lox in him—Lox was the son of Evil, and it was known that he sometimes took the form of a badger.

A fearless and impudent rascal, Badger lived a carefree life on the labor of others, having no time from merrymaking to spend on hunting. Finally, however, his neighbors grew tired of supporting him. One summer when food was scarce, the chief of Badger's tribe said to him, "You take all and give nothing. We can no longer afford to share our meat with you. We have decided to give you enough food for half a moon's journey. You will then be too far away to trouble us, and you will have to live as you can."

"Who will take care of Little Brother when I am gone?" Badger demanded. You see, Badger was not all bad. He had a small brother who was gentle and shy and not very clever, and ever since the boys had lost their parents, Badger had looked after Little Brother and treated him with affection.

"He will be given a home with foster parents," said the chief, but Little Brother burst into tears.

"I want to go with my brother," he wailed.

"Very well, then come along," said Badger. He grinned saucily at the villagers. "Thank you, my friends, for giving us a chance to see the world!" he said. Then, with all their possessions in a blanket slung over Badger's shoulder, the two set jauntily off into the woods. However, they did not go far. Badger stopped before the mouth of a small cave and told Little Brother to go inside.

"The food will last you until the full of the moon, when I shall return," he said. "I want to play one last trick on our late friends."

Badger dressed himself in the beads and feathers of a medicine man and put a mask on his face. He knew that at the time his tribe had no medicine man, so he went back to the village and announced that he was a powerful man of magic. His old neighbors did not recognize Badger and treated him with great respect. They gave him a wigwam to live in and shared their food with him, begging him to treat their sick and use his magic to make meat more plentiful.

For a while Badger played the role of medicine man with glee. He beat his drum and shook his rattle and pretended to summon spirits. He sold charms and fell into trances, and all the time, behind his mask, he was laughing. However, game in the district grew scarcer and scarcer, and as the people grew hungrier and hungrier, they began to lose faith in their medicine man.

One day, near the full of the moon, a long, loud wail came from the forest. The people shook with fear, but not Badger, who knew at once what it meant. It was Little Brother crying because he was lonely and his food was gone. The wail was heard again. "It is the giant Famine," said Badger with a long face. "He says he is coming to this village."

The people began to groan with dismay.

"Never fear," said Badger calmly. "I, your medicine man, will go out to meet him and drive him away. Give me a bag of tallow," said Badger, "to take with me, for I shall need plenty of strength to defeat the fellow."

Tallow was a great delicacy in the olden times. It was made by pounding and breaking the bones of a moose, then boiling the bones until the grease came to the top. The grease, a white substance, hard as wax, was then skimmed off with a wooden spoon. It was a nourishing food, and hunters used to take it with them on long expeditions as their only provision. So the people gave Badger a bag of tallow, the last they had, and off he went, crying out in a commanding voice, "*Ahhhhhh chowwwwwwwwwaaa!*" The people thought this a cry of defiance against the giant, but it was really the secret name Badger had for his brother, to let him know he was coming.

The villagers waited and listened for the sounds of battle, but they heard nothing. Then they waited long—and in vain —for the return of their medicine man.

Deep in the forest, Badger and Little Brother were feasting on the tallow, laughing together at Badger's cleverness. Suddenly they heard a rushing sound in the forest. Badger jumped up, alarmed, as huge feet came crashing through the underbrush. The trees swayed as a great hand flung them aside, and all at once a fearsome giant stood before the brothers. His face was as green as the grass, and his hair sprang out from his huge head like needles on pine boughs. Before Badger knew what was happening, the green giant had seized Little Brother in his mighty green hand and stuffed him into the bag he carried on his shoulder.

"Save me," shrieked Little Brother.

Badger jumped upon the giant furiously, biting, punching and kicking, but the giant only laughed. "What is tickling my legs?" he asked.

"Give me back my little brother," stormed Badger.

"Certainly," said the green giant, "as soon as you bring me the magic food of Glooscap, which never grows less no matter how much of it is eaten."

Poor Badger stared at the giant in dismay. It was a long way to Blomidon, where Glooscap lived, and the path to it was full of danger. Moreover, there was no certainty that Glooscap would give him the food when he got there.

"I shall wait for you here," the green giant said, shouting. "But only for the space of time it takes the sun to run its full course. If you do not bring the food by then, I will have to eat Little Brother instead."

Without a word, Badger set off through the trees at top speed. Late that day, tired and breathless, he reached the shore of Minas Basin and looked up at Blomidon's red slopes, immense against the darkening sky. He knew, in order to find Glooscap's lodge, he must climb to the very top. He was terribly tired and yearned to rest, but the thought of Little Brother in the hands of the green giant drove him up the red slope as fast as possible.

The red stone was slippery and covered him with red dust, but he kept on. Branches of low spruce and juniper scratched his face and tore his hands, but he paid no attention. His lungs pained; his head throbbed. His throat was hot and dry as he dragged himself the last few yards and tumbled over full length on the grass at the summit. Too worn out for a moment to move, Badger lay still, recovering his breath. Then he got wearily to his feet. There stood Glooscap's great wigwam, a fire dimly glowing within. The great chief himself was nowhere in sight, nor was there any sign of Noogumee, Glooscap's grandmother, or of Marten, his servant. Badger could not wait for their return to ask for food—there was no time. Besides, the great chief might refuse to give it to him. Badger must get the food somehow and hurry back to the green giant.

He crept into the lodge and looked around, then cried out softly. A dish of Glooscap's magic food stood beside the fire. He had only to reach out and take it, but as his fingers curved around the dish, they were struck aside.

"Stop, thief!" a stern voice commanded. And Badger looked up to see the great Glooscap towering over him. But his fear for Little Brother was even greater than his fear of the great chief.

"Oh, please, master! Give me the magic food, for I must save my brother from the green giant!"

"Why should I give you anything?" asked Glooscap. "You who have robbed and tricked your neighbors?"

"You can't let Little Brother die!" Badger cried. "It wasn't his fault. If you don't help me, the giant will eat him!"

"Will he?" asked Glooscap mysteriously, and before Badger's surprised eyes, Glooscap began to change. His skin became green, his hair stood out from his head in green spikes, and his green face assumed a ferocious expression.

"You are the green giant!" gasped Badger.

"And I hope he has taught you a lesson," said Glooscap, looking himself again. "Are you sorry for the way you behaved?"

"Yes, indeed!" cried Badger.

"And will you promise to give up your silly tricks and do your share of hunting?"

"I will, I will, if only—"

"Then look behind you."

Badger turned and saw Little Brother, smiling and unharmed, standing beside the fire. So great was Badger's relief he nearly cried. For the first time, too, he realized how tired he was and how hungry. The old impudent grin appeared. "I don't suppose," he suggested, "that you could spare *me* a bit of that food?"

"Certainly not!" Glooscap said indignantly, "not until you can share it with the people you robbed of their tallow. Take this food to them at once. It will never grow less, no matter how much is eaten, until game is again plentiful in the forest."

When the people of Badger's old village saw him bringing the magic food of Glooscap, they forgave him and welcomed him back into the tribe. Famine no longer troubled the villagers, and Badger behaved himself for quite some time.

But if you think he had played his last trick, you are mistaken, for in time you will hear again of Badger and his mischief-making.

Until then, *kespeadooksit!*

—From Glooscap and His Magic by Kay Hill

Notes and Sources

NOTES

THE IROQUOIS

The Talking Stone Several Indian tribes have a story about a rock that imparts the legends of the people to those who will listen so that these tales can be perpetuated. Gus-Tah-Ote is the Spirit of the Rock and storyteller in this Seneca version.

Sky Elk, the Ghost of Whiteface Mountain Whiteface Mountain, near Saranac in New York State, has inspired many legends, as has a ghostly creature reportedly seen by the Iroquois over the decades.

Turkey Brother and the Magic Panther Suit This is one of a number of tales which involve Turkey Brother.

CENTRAL AND NORTHEAST WOODLAND

Thunderbird More than an explanation of thunder and lightning, this story shows the intense love of the Native Americans in the Woodland area for their lakes and forests, frequently the background of Manabozho tales.

Little Burnt Face Among the Native American tribes there are many variants of Cinderella. This particular version is rooted in Micmac and Passamaquoddy culture.

Ojeeg, the Hunter, and the Ice Man The cold, long winters of the Northeast inspired many stories; the seasons were often personified, as winter is in the Ice Man.

SOUTHEAST

The Theft of Fire Sly, weak Rabbit, southeastern trickster, was beneficent as well as mischievous. This tale is from the Hitchiti tribe, in the Creek Confederacy of the South.

Spearfinger, the Witch U-tlun-ta, the terrible witch who survived on human livers, is the central figure in this "Wonder Tale," which begins, as did most Cherokee stories, "This is what the old men told me when I was a boy. . . ." James Mooney, who lived among the Cherokee and studied their folklore for many years, recorded it.

SOUTHWEST

Foot Racers of Payupki Running and gambling were famous among the Hopi tribes. This tale is unusual in featuring a girl heroine. Historical events are the basis for many of the Hopi's stories, and this explains the removal of the old village of Payupki to another mesa.

Why Blackbird Has White Eyes Among the many Navajo stories, usually long and involved, there are also the shorter trickster tales of Coyote and his foil, Big-Long-Man (a farmer), or some other animal. Hosten Clah Chee, from whom this "why" tale comes, was a renowned storyteller.

A hogan is the traditional six-to-eight-sided earth-and-log dwelling of the Navajo people.

The month of Slender Wind comes during the winter and is the time the fire ceremony takes place.

The Summer Birds of K'yakime Zuñi Creation myths are often an integral part of their ceremonials, and this typical story recounts the miraculous birth of a hero and the origin of bird appearances.

PLAINS

Iktomi and the Ducks This is a trickster tale, widely known, in which the trickster captures geese, prairie dogs, or ducks for his dinner by distracting them. Here he achieves his end by teaching them a new dance. Iktomi is the tiny brown spider man of the Dakota people.

Small Star and the Mud Pony The Skidi Pawnee felt special reverence toward their god Tirawa. They also had a close relationship with the earth and the stars, by which they were greatly influenced. Their love of horses and good horsemanship was pronounced, and all these interests are reflected in this story.

PLATEAU-CALIFORNIA

Skinkoots Steals the Springtime The Kutenai trickster, Skinkoots, the coyote, was a popular rascal, the center of a score of tales of which this is one of the favorites.

Manitou was a name for the Great Spirit; it was also a supernatural power or a magic native force which a brave might possess.

What Happened to Six Wives Who Ate Onions California tales, often very short, frequently explained the origin of some natural phenomenon—a mountain, the constellations, a rock formation. This typical story reflects the importance of the family and explains the Pleiades.

Coyote and the Swallowing Monster Stories of an enormous serpentlike creature that devoured men and animals were widespread among the Plateau tribes. The trickster in this tale destroys the monster, but at the same time explains the origin of many of the tribes.

Cottontail Plays a Trick on Coyote The California cottontail is a saucy, long-legged, and quick-witted trickster, often the foil for Coyote. He is somewhat more brazen than the Cherokee cottontail!

PACIFIC NORTHWEST

The Feast of the Mountain Goats Totems were of such importance in this area that the discovery of a new family crest created great interest. In this story the origin of the one-horned mountain goat totem is explained.

Raven and the Nose of the Gonaqadet The existence of a deep-sea monster was accepted by many Pacific tribes. Raven, the trickster, in a scrape of his own making, blunders into him.

Halibut Man and the House on the Waves The stress in this tale, as in so many others told by people where food is a constant concern, is how to provide for the future. The salmon run—so vital to the coastal tribes—is featured in this story.

Oolachen is a small oily fish, a member of the salmon family highly valued by the people of the Pacific coastal tribes.

FAR NORTH AND ESKIMO

The-Boy-Who-Snared-the-Wind and the Shaman's Daughter Because existence is so precarious in the Arctic, courage and endurance are highly prized. The story reveals the boy's daring as well as the trickery of the shaman in this very ancient tale of unknown origin. It may have outlived many Eskimo tales because it has more plot than most.

A parfleche is a rawhide carrying case.

The Angakok and the Mother of Seals The needs of the land children are conveyed to the Mother of Seals through the Angakok's spirit power. The story reflects the starkness of the Eskimos' life.

The Day Tuk Became a Hunter The Eskimo boy was given the status of an adult in the community when, by his own skill and with his own weapons, he could demonstrate that he could provide food for his family. Tuk also saved the life of his family.

CANADA

The Boy Who Was Called Thickhead English, French, and Scandinavian influences may be traced in the stories of the Maritime tribes. This tale is reminiscent of many European folktales in which the youngest son achieves success through luck, pluck, and a little magic.

Why Bootup, the Whale, Smokes a Pipe Legends about the kindly Glooscap all attest to his generous nature and concern for his children, animal and otherwise, for in those days each understood the other. The cycle of Glooscap tales is almost endless.

A dice platter was a small wooden plate upon which the dice were thrown in games of chance.

The Magic Snowshoes Some of the customs and the language of the Wabenaki (Abenaki) tribes is revealed in this Glooscap tale.

Badger and the Green Giant Badger often plays the role of mischievous foil in many of the Glooscap stories, and in this he not only gets his comeuppance but discovers the great one in one of his shape-changing roles.

kespeadooksit, "and now the story ends."

SOURCES

THE IROQUOIS

The Talking Stone

Converse, Harriet M. *Myths and Legends of the New York State Iroquois* (ed. A. C. Parker, New York State Museum, Bulletin 125), Albany, University of State of N.Y., 1908, pp. 66 ff.

Curtin, Jeremiah. *Seneca Indian Myths*, New York, Dutton, 1923. See "The Origin of Stories."

Curtin, Jeremiah, and Hewitt, J. N. B. "The Story of Hahskwahot," in *Seneca Fiction, Legends, and Myths* (Bureau of American Ethnology, 32nd Annual Report), Washington, D.C., 1910–1911.

Parker, Arthur Caswell. *Seneca Myths and Folk Tales*, Buffalo (New York) Historical Society, 1923.

Sky Elk, the Ghost of Whiteface Mountain

Browne, G. Waldo. "The Shadow Moose," in *Indian Nights*, New York, Noble and Noble, 1927.

Converse, Harriet M. "O-je-a-neh-doh, the Sky-Elk," in *Myths and Legends of the New York State Iroquois* (ed. A. C. Parker, New York State Museum, Bulletin 125), Albany, University of State of N.Y., 1908.

Turkey Brother and the Magic Panther Suit

Curtin, Jeremiah. *Seneca Indian Myths*, New York, Dutton, 1923.

Parker, Arthur Caswell. *Seneca Myths and Legends*, Buffalo (New York), Historical Society, 1923.

CENTRAL AND NORTHEAST WOODLAND

Thunderbird

Chafetz, Henry. *The Thunderbird and Other Stories*, New York, Pantheon, 1964.

Little Burnt Face

Leland, Charles. "The Invisible One," in *The Algonquin Legends*, Boston, Houghton, 1884.

Rand, Silas T. *Legends of the Micmacs*, New York, Longmans Green, 1894.

Ojeeg, the Hunter, and the Ice Man

Schoolcraft, Henry. *Algic Researches*, New York, 1839.

Rand, Silas T. *Legends of the Micmacs*, New York, Longmans Green, 1894.

SOUTHEAST

The Theft of Fire

Swanton, J. R. *Myths of the Southeast Indians* (Bureau of American Ethnology, Bulletin 88), Washington, D.C., Government Printing Office, 1928.

Spearfinger, the Witch

Bell, Corydon. *John Rattling-Gourd*, New York, Macmillan Publishing Co., Inc., 1955.

Mooney, James. *Myths of the Cherokees* (Bureau of American Ethnology, 19th Annual Report, Part I), Washington, D.C. 1897–1898.

SOUTHWEST

Foot Racers of Payupki

Courlander, Harold. *People of the Short Blue Corn: Tales and Legends of the Hopi Indians*, New York, Harcourt Brace Jovanovich, 1970. The author has made transcriptions from oral sources, and done his own collecting and retelling.

Why Blackbird Has White Eyes

Chee, Hosteen Clah. *Navajo Bird Tales*, Wheaton (Ill.), Theosophical Publishing House, 1970. The author says the story was told to her by native storytellers who came to the trading post she and her husband directed on the Navajo Reservation.

The Summer Birds of K'yakime

Cushing, Frank, *Zuñi Folk Tales*, New York, Putnam, 1901.
Nusbaum, Aileen. *Zuñi Indian Tales*, New York, Putnam, 1928.

PLAINS

Iktomi and the Ducks

Eastman, Charles and Elaine. "Unktomee and His Bundle of Song" in *Wigwam Evenings*, Boston, Little Brown, 1909, 1937.
Zitkala-Sa. *Old Indian Legends*, Boston, Ginn, 1901.

Small Star and the Mud Pony

Dorsey, George A. *Traditions of the Skidi Pawnee* (American Folklore Society), Boston, Houghton, 1904, pp. 152–156.

PLATEAU-CALIFORNIA

Skinkoots Steals the Springtime

Boas, Franz. "Origin of the Seasons," in *Kutenai Tales* (Bureau of American Ethnology, Bulletin 59), Washington, D.C., Government Printing Office, 1918.
Linderman, Frank. *Kootenai Why-Stories*, New York, Scribner, 1926.

What Happened to Six Wives Who Ate Onions

Fisher, Anne. *Stories California Indians Told*, Berkeley (Cal.), Parnassus, 1957; now Boston, Houghton.
Latta, F. F. "'Kotch-Pih-Lah, the Pleiades," in *California Indian Folklore*, Shafter, Cal., 1936.

Coyote and the Swallowing Monster

Boas, Franz. "Folktales of the Salishan and Sahaptin," in *Memoirs of the American Folklore Society*, Vol. XI, 1917.

Phinney, Archie. "Coyote and the Monster," in *Nez Percé Texts*, New York, Columbia University Press, 1934.

Cottontail Plays a Trick on Coyote

Stevenson, Matilda C. "Sia Myths" (Bureau of American Ethnology, 11th Annual Report), Washington, D.C., Government Printing Office, 1889–1890, pp. 147 ff.

PACIFIC NORTHWEST

The Feast of the Mountain Goats

Boas, Franz. "Tsimshian Mythology" (Bureau of American Ethnology, 31st Annual Report), Washington, D.C., Government Printing Office, 1909–1910.

Raven and the Nose of the Gonaqadet

Boas, Franz. "Tsimshian Mythology" (Bureau of American Ethnology, 31st Annual Report), Washington, D.C., Government Printing Office, 1909–1910.

Swanton, J. R. "Tlingit Myths and Texts" (Bureau of American Ethnology, Bulletin 39), Washington, D.C., Government Printing Office, 1909.

———. "Haida Texts and Myths" (Bureau of American Ethnology, Bulletin 29), Washington, D.C., Government Printing Office, 1905.

Teit, James. "Tahlten Tales" in *Journal of American Folklore* (American Folklore Society), Vol. 32, 1919, p. 224.

Halibut Man and the House on the Waves

Boas, Franz. "Bella Bella Tales" in *Memoirs of American Folklore Society*, Vol. XXV, 1932.

———. "Bella Bella Texts" in *Columbia Contributions to Anthropology*, New York, Columbia University Press, 1928.

———. "Tsimshian Mythology" (Bureau of American Ethnology, 31st Annual Report), Washington, D.C., Government Printing Office, 1909–1910.

FAR NORTH AND ESKIMO

The Boy-Who-Snared-the-Wind and the Shaman's Daughter

American Folklore Society. "Traditions of the Thompson River Indians," in *Memoirs of American Folklore Society*, Boston, Houghton Mifflin, 1898.

Teit, James, and Boas, Franz. "Mythology of the Thompson River

Indians" in *American Museum of Natural History Memoirs*, Vol.
VIII; Jesup North Pacific Expedition, p. 393–394, titled "Sna'-
naz and the Shaman."

The Angakok and the Mother of Seals

Boas, Franz. "Central Eskimoes" (Bureau of American Ethnology,
6th Annual Report), Washington, D.C., Government Printing
Office, 1888, pp. 583–585.

Carpenter, Frances. *Wonder Tales of Seas and Ships*, Garden City,
N.Y., Doubleday, 1964.

The Day Tuk Became a Hunter

Boas, Franz. *Memoirs of the American Museum of Natural History*,
Vol. 15, Part I, 1901; Part II, 1907.

Melzack, Ronald. *The Day Tuk Became a Hunter*, New York, Dodd,
Mead, 1968.

CANADA

The Boy Who Was Called Thickhead

Macmillan, Cyrus. *Canadian Wonder Tales*, London, The Bodley
Head.

Why Bootup, the Whale, Smokes a Pipe

Leland, C. G., and Prince, J. D. *Kulascap, the Master*, New York,
Funk and Wagnalls, 1902, pp. 165 ff.

——. *Algonquin Legends*, 2nd ed., Boston, Houghton, 1884.

The Magic Snowshoes

Hill, Kay, *More Glooscap Stories*, New York, Dodd, Mead, 1970.

Badger and the Green Giant

Hill, Kay. *Glooscap and His Magic*, New York, Dodd, Mead, 1968.

Acknowledgments

Thanks are due to the following for permission to include copyrighted material:

The Bodley Head, for "The Boy Who Was Called Thickhead" from *Canadian Wonder Tales,* collected by Cyrus Macmillan.

Dodd, Mead & Company, Inc., and McClelland and Stewart Limited, Toronto, for "The Day Tuk Became a Hunter" from *The Day Tuk Became a Hunter and Other Stories* by Ronald Melzack, Copyright © 1968 by Ronald Melzack.

Dodd, Mead & Company, Inc., McClelland and Stewart Limited, Toronto, and Curtis Brown, Ltd., for "The Magic Snowshoes" from *More Glooscap Stories* by Kay Hill, Copyright © 1970 by Kay Hill.

Dodd, Mead & Company, Inc., McClelland and Stewart Limited, Toronto, and A. P. Watt Ltd. for Kay Hill, for "Badger and the Green Giant" from *Glooscap and His Magic* by Kay Hill, Copyright © 1968 by Kay Hill.

Doubleday & Company, Inc., for "The Angakok and the Mother of Seals" from *Wonder Tales of Seas and Ships* by Frances Carpenter, Copyright © 1959 by Frances Carpenter Huntington.

Harcourt Brace Jovanovich, Inc., for "The Foot-Racer of Payupki" from *People of the Short Blue Corn: Tales and Legends of the Hopi Indians,* Copyright © 1970 by Harold Courlander.

Houghton Mifflin Company, for "What Happened to Six Wives Who Ate Onions" from *Stories California Indians Told* by Anne B. Fisher, Copyright 1957 by Anne B. Fisher.

Macmillan Publishing Co., Inc., for "Spearfinger the Witch" from *John Rattling-Gourd* by Corydon Bell, Copyright © 1955 by Macmillan Publishing Co., Inc.

Pantheon Books, a Division of Random House, Inc., and McIntosh and Otis, Inc., for "The Thunderbird," adapted by permission of Pantheon Books from *The Thunderbird and Other Stories* by Henry Chafetz, Copyright © 1964 by Henry Chafetz and Ronni Solbert.

G. P. Putnam's Sons, for "The Summer Birds of K'yakime" from *Zuñi Indian Tales* by Aileen Nusbaum, Copyright 1928 by Aileen Nusbaum.

Theosophical Publishing House, Wheaton, Illinois, for "Why the Blackbird Has White Eyes" from *Navajo Bird Tales* by Hosteen Clah Chee, Copyright 1970.